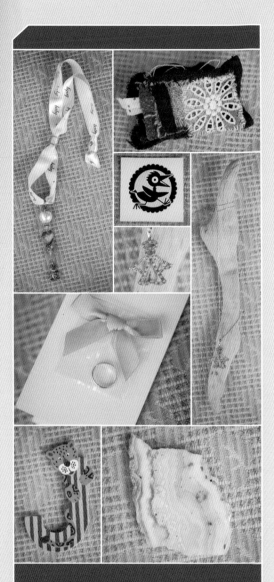

Simple objects were lovingly collected during one family's experience with miscarriage. Each item was carefully placed in this special glass jar, forming what the baby's parents call an *altar*.

Meaningful Moments:
Ritual and Reflection
When a Child Dies

Rana Limbo & Kathie Kobler

Meaningful Moments: Ritual and Reflection When a Child Dies
Rana Limbo and Kathie Kobler

Published by Bereavement and Advance Care Planning Services
Gundersen Medical Foundation
1900 South Avenue
La Crosse, WI 54601
www.bereavementservices.org

ISBN 978-0-615-79080-0
First Edition

Edited by Charlotte Grant
Layout & Design by Joe McCormick

Photography by:
Roger A. Grant - rogeragrant.photoshelter.com *(pages ix, x, 5, 7, 13, 14, 19, 20, 29, 31, 32, 35, 40, 47, 51, 55, 61, 65, 71, 76, 77, 83)*
Todd Hochberg - toddhochberg.com *(pages 24, 26, 27, 39, 42, 74)*
Kristin Royalty – Gundersen Health System *(pages 8, 17, 59, 62, 67)*
Brooke Doval – Gundersen Health System *(inside front cover)*
Jim Tritch – Gundersen Health System *(pages 56, 57)*
Heather J. Silver – Chesapeake Kids, Annapolis, MD *(page 23)*
Jessi Hill – Hill Photography and Artwork *(page 60)*
Jim Marvy – *(page 58)*
Contributed Family Photos *(pages 25, 36, 52, 57, 58)*

"A Caregiver's Song of Lament," "Because of Logan," and *"On Rocking Arthur."* Copyright Kathie Kobler. Used with permission.

Additional copies of this book may be ordered at www.bereavementservices.org.

Printed in the United States of America

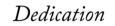

Dedication

To the children, families, and colleagues who have
shared many meaningful moments with us.

Acknowledgements

We thank those who have so willingly shared their stories of ritual and relationship. We are grateful to Charlotte Grant who served as our editor. We express our deep gratitude to Roger Grant, Rana's friend for nearly 35 years, whose beautiful work adorns the walls of her home and now this book, a photographic artist extraordinaire. The Grant's grandson, Benjamin, was stillborn while they worked on this book. We honor his memory through these pages. Thank you to Todd Hochberg whose eye for capturing meaningful moments in photos inspired our writing. Danai Papadatou, author of the foreword, a friend and colleague, graced us with her beautiful and inspiring words. We acknowledge, with grateful hearts, our own families and close friends who bring richness and fulfillment to our lives every day.

Table of Contents

Foreword

To read *Meaningful Moments: Ritual and Reflection When a Child Dies* is to embark on a journey of reflection over profound life losses and ritual that are helpful in marking a passage from living with a seriously ill baby or child, to living in his or her absence. It is a book about acknowledging and transforming a deep suffering that is evoked by the reality of a pregnancy ending too soon or a child's death. Such death often appears incomprehensible and unfair, as it reverses the perceived order of nature, with children dying before their parents and grandparents.

This book challenges the common perinatal and pediatric practices in many acute care hospitals and ambulatory settings of *medicalizing* the dying process and *de-ritualizing* death. Death without ritual deprives families of symbolic activities that facilitate separation and validate grief.

Rana Limbo and Kathie Kobler offer an alternative approach that underscores the importance of *companioning* families through critical life transitions. The authors invite professionals to become the family's companions by helping seriously ill infants and children pave a dignified way out of life while preparing parents, siblings, and grandparents for separation, and by supporting them through their grief. Drawing on their long nursing experience in perinatal and pediatric nursing, the authors do something unique. They propose a framework for planning and performing rituals that are meaningful to families whose child is dying or is deceased, and provide guidelines on how to create opportunities for "meaningful moments" that transform suffering. They move beyond rituals that are prescribed or preordained by culture and religious traditions. They invite clinicians, with the help of guided questions, to assess each family's beliefs, values, preferences, and needs before joining parents, siblings, and significant others in *co-creating* and *actively participating* in rituals that are meaningful to them.

Rituals represent highly symbolic acts of significance that confer transcendental meaning on the loss experience. Whether practiced in private or with others, whether arising in the moment or planned in advance, they are most helpful when they meet the following functions:

- *affirm the imminence or reality of a pregnancy's ending or child's death*

- *provide opportunities for expressing feelings without necessarily resorting to words*

- *attribute a transcending meaning and offer alternative explanations that help family members understand the child's death within the context of their beliefs*

- *legitimize the continuity of the relationship with the deceased child and celebrate his or her life no matter how brief it is or may have been, and*

- *validate grief by reinforcing mutual support and solidarity among the mourners who integrate the bereaved family into the larger community.*

The authors provide a wealth of examples of ritual: *rituals of welcome* for an expected baby who is born with a life-threatening condition; *rituals of separation* that provide opportunities for good-byes and expressions of love; *rituals of affirmation* of the child's unique characteristics, talents, and impact upon the family's life; and *rituals of continuity* that recognize the on-going connection with the deceased child and the reconstruction of the family's story, which has been shattered by loss.

The book also comprises a section that addresses the effects on professionals of caring for babies and children who die. It underlines the significance of creating collective rituals that acknowledge the clinicians' losses and grief, and provide opportunities for mutual support. Through the sharing of personal experiences, Rana Limbo and Kathie Kobler demonstrate in an admirable way that there are no limits to the creativity and ingenuity of ritualized acts that celebrate valued relationships and honor a child's life. Their words reflect how the rewards of caring for those whose pregnancy ends too soon, whose baby is born still, or whose child is dying stem from the poignancy of "present moments" that professionals share with families in the face of death. These "meaningful moments" are not measurable, but fully lived; they render the reality of loss more bearable, meaningful, and—whenever experienced as "extra-ordinary"—are carried in memory forever.

Meaningful Moments: Ritual and Reflection When a Child Dies makes a significant contribution to the field of dying, death, and bereavement by filling an existing void in the literature that has disregarded the power of personalized rituals to contain and transform suffering in meaningful ways. It is written with sensitivity, compassion, and wisdom. This book is a gift to families and those who care for them. In addition, it is an invaluable resource for administrators and other leaders who ensure high quality care at their sites, and seek opportunities for staff development and support. This challenging book opens up avenues for reflection on personalized rituals that honor relationships and enrich the lives of those who co-create and perform them.

Danai Papadatou, PhD, MEd
Professor of Clinical Psychology
Faculty of Nursing
University of Athens, Greece

Dr. Papadatou's clinical experience, research interests, and publications focus mostly on issues related to pediatric palliative care, bereavement support, and community disasters. She is also the president of "Merimna," a Greek non-governmental organization, which provides pediatric palliative home care services and bereavement support to children, families, and school communities that are affected by death. She has received various awards for her clinical, research, and educational contributions in the field of death, dying, and bereavement.

Ritual: 99 days with Eliot

At 30 weeks pregnant my wife, Ginny, and I were told that our child had a condition that meant he or she would most likely not make it to birth, and—if we were so blessed with a birth—then there was a high likelihood that the life would be a short one. This unwelcomed news set our lives on a different trajectory in so many ways. One of the ways, which was never actually discussed or acknowledged by either of us, but seemed to flow naturally from our new reality, was a deep desire to anchor our world within the present.

When Eliot did come, we were transferred to the NICU, where we sat holding him while surrounded by other tiny, fragile lives. We were discussing to ourselves how the clock was creeping toward 4:59 p.m. and how he had been with us for 24 hours, his first unpromised day. Minutes later, one of the nurses quietly came alongside us with what she called a "birthday hat," a small circle of tinsel she had heisted from a nearby bulletin board celebrating the 4th of July. She proceeded to hand the sleep-deprived new parents, as well as each nurse, a piece of "birthday cake," otherwise known as breath mints, for Eliot's party. We laughed at her ingenuity as all who were present gathered around to sing happy birthday in hushed tones; such a familiar song rang out in such an unfamiliar setting.

With Eliot, some sort of camera was an integral part of the goods that became his traveling posse: typical baby items such as diapers and wipes, a portable oxygen tank, a mechanized device for help with his tube feeding and always a camera. We were full of fear and knew that looking ahead might sink us; so we desperately sought help with living in the moments that we were given. That camera always came out around 4:59 each day as we had a birthday for every day of Eliot's life from then on. We got 99 birthdays with Eliot and though I am left wishing for more, I am thankful for a woman whose quick and tender actions helped us see that practices and parties can help one celebrate and—more importantly—live within the moments we are given.

Ritual, for us, became a way to take the smallest of steps toward thankfulness. There were things to be thankful for, but without intentionality they were eclipsed by our sadness and left unacknowledged. For us, ritual was not a way out; we miss him every day. Ritual is a way in— into the moments that we did receive. These practices that we had when he was here now help us to continue on with this journey that has no map.

And when there is no map, the smallest anchor to that present moment and now to a former reality—indeed, to a person that we love beyond measure—this tether becomes a means to bind you to what you will never forget. Ritual has served as a way to remind us and others that what we see is not all there is or was or, I believe, will be.

Matt Mooney

The film "99 Balloons" honors the brief but remarkable life of Eliot, son of Matthew and Ginny Mooney. With nearly 4 million YouTube views, a featured spot on the Oprah Winfrey Show, and a place in the Resolve Through Sharing® Bereavement Training: Perinatal Death, the Mooneys' film has touched more lives than they ever imagined. Eliot and his family are powerful examples of ritual, relationship, and hope. To view the video, visit Matt's blog, and learn about an organization the Mooneys created to help other families with medically fragile children receive respite care, go to: *http://www.99balloons.org/history.php*

From the authors

As nurses, we have seen the power of ritual transform human experience. Several years ago, we collaborated on an article on ritual that led to the writing of this book. Now we write to honor the relationships and experiences of ritual in our personal and professional lives.

We believe ritual unfolds from relationship, an idea that resonates with others. Often in our follow-up bereavement work, families convey stories of interactions that allowed them to connect with their dying baby or child in significant ways. When healthcare professionals are asked what provides meaning in their work, they recount moments of honoring the child-parent relationship in the midst of tremendous sorrow and suffering. Transformation is the common thread in these stories. Participants emerge from ritual with hearts changed.

This book is for

- *Caregivers who may introduce parents to its ideas, images, and poetry*

- *Caregivers seeking ways to recognize and co-create meaningful moments*

- *Families whose beloved child dies*

- *Anyone interested in reflecting on the spiritual dimensions of life centered in relationship with others*

- *All who participate in human experiences that tap our deepest emotions*

We hope our idea that ritual can be created in the moment will also resonate with you. May you find your own personal stories of relationship, hope, and love reflected in these pages. We wish for you the discovery of meaningful moments today and every day.

Rana Limbo
La Crosse, WI

Kathie Kobler
Buffalo Grove, IL

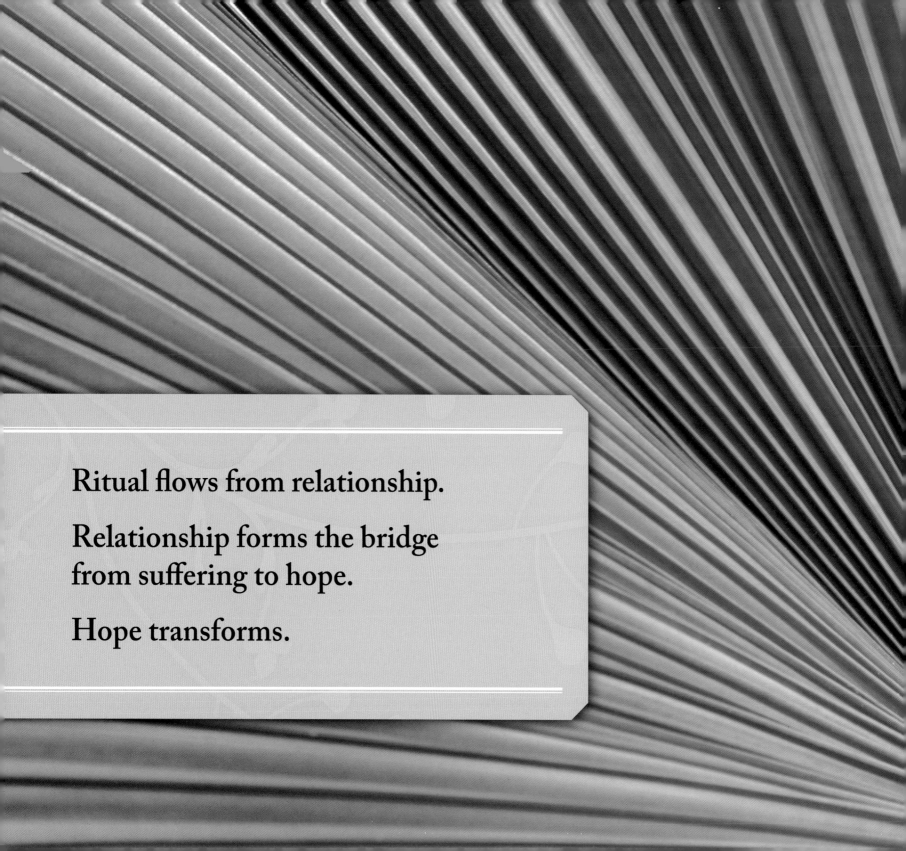

Ritual flows from relationship.

Relationship forms the bridge
from suffering to hope.

Hope transforms.

Introduction

Deep within all human interactions are moments that define an experience. Each is an instant in time that captures the essence of all that is unfolding.

Deep within each of us is a corresponding instinct to recognize these special moments… to bring significance and meaning to the powerful interactions that emerge from relationship.

This book is about honoring those moments when the death of a child permanently changes a relationship both assumed to be and dreamed of as living and lasting. It is about parents, families, and caregivers making time to watch, listen, and interact. It is about sharing all the feelings and experiences that encompass the hard work of saying goodbye to a beloved child.

It is about what lies within—and ahead—for the heart of each person changed by a life ended too soon.

This book is about ritual *and* reflection

In keeping with that theme, we include reflections from parents. Their stories may not contain ritual, yet they are profoundly moving in describing the transformative nature of grief.

You will find points for reflection throughout the book. They are intended to help you internalize and personalize its precepts. Developing a reflective practice helps balance life and work, enhancing the intimacy of caring for others.[1] We invite you to pause and reflect on the questions we pose. You may want to write in the spaces provided or simply be open to the thoughts and feelings that arise. As you ponder the questions, the answers may lead you to action. Some of the questions and/or answers may be anchor points, helping you transition to what comes next.

As a guide for reflection, we offer the *PRAM* framework. We believe this 4-step process of self-awareness and preparation is an ideal way to learn and practice the art of reflection. Taking time to *be* in the midst of *doing* requires a thoughtful approach.

PAUSE

Stop. Be still. Center yourself. Focus on something in your environment, such as the door card marking the room you are about to enter. Ground yourself. Feel your feet on the floor.

REFLECT

Think about your breathing. Pay attention as your chest rises and falls. Think about the situation you are about to encounter. Think about what a relationship might look like between you and the person you are about to meet or see. Reflect on your feelings.

ACKNOWLEDGE

Name what you feel. Tell yourself it's OK to feel as you do.

BE **M**INDFUL

Be in the moment by bringing your full attention and energy to the meaning of the relationship that has brought you here. Silently bless the space.

PRAM © 2012. Kathie Kobler and Gundersen Medical Foundation

Reflection:

Before you begin reading the pages of this book, pause for a moment.

Close your eyes, take a deep breath. Let your mind wander to an event

in your life that was significant. Spend a few minutes remembering.

When you are finished, turn the page.

Reflection:

Was there ritual in your remembering? What does the word "ritual" mean to you?

Memories of a meaningful past event generally include ritual. Rituals are significant because they prompt us to recall and reflect, acting as touchstones to our past. Ritual has permanence, created in the moment and called to mind and heart at a later time. The memory links the present with the past, making ritual a powerful way to maintain lasting bonds with someone who died.

Rituals are common to all cultures. They may be sacred or secular and have been used to mark transitions, establish order, and promote healing.[2-5] According to Rando,[6(p. 402)] ritual is a "specific behavior or activity that gives symbolic expression to certain feelings and thoughts." Authors write about the power of ritual to transform,[7] offering an avenue for family members to create new connections with the deceased.[8-11] Anderson[2] writes specifically about using ritual to meet the needs of a dying person.

A ritual has a beginning, middle, and end. Because ritual involves different senses, memories of past rituals can be evoked in different ways. You might remember a loved one's funeral ritual by what the weather was like, the scent of a single gardenia, the sound of a piece of music, or the emotion you felt when you said good-bye for the last time.

There is power in ritual whether it occurs with a group of people or in solitude. A woman whose baby died early in pregnancy may plant a colorful flower in her baby's memory in her private garden and later participate in a community memory walk that brings together hundreds of bereaved parents.

Many think of ritual as actions or prayers associated with religious ceremonies. A broader understanding of ritual from a spiritual perspective, which may or may not include religious practices, opens up the possibilities of where and how ritual can be created.[12] Ritual occurs in the moment, but transcends the here and now by spiritually connecting participants at a deeper, mindful level, touching the core of our existence.[13]

The Power of a Moment

Ritual is about a single "elongated moment,"[8] created out of relationship, to build a bridge from despair to hope and wholeness. Exemplary oncology nurses reported on the importance of "moments" as a way of remaining engaged in the work of caring for the dying. Specifically, they spoke of moments of connection, making moments matter, and energizing moments with their patients.[14] Being mindful of the moment is the foundation of the PRAM framework. Whether pausing to admire a dying baby's hands or acknowledging the moment when a father's hope shifts to wanting a peaceful death for his son, each is a mental or emotional snapshot that can be brought to mind well after the experience passes. Parents and caregivers who look for, wait for, and pay attention to those moments allow ritual to emerge, transforming the here and now into something that is forever.

The Role of Ritual When a Child Dies

While ritual doesn't "fix" or "complete" a person's grief, it uniquely facilitates connection to the one who died and all who share that loss.

Very little has been written about ritual and its usefulness for families when a child dies. Ritual is defined as a spontaneous or created response that marks a significant point in time. Throughout this book we describe how ritual can be a part of the meaningful moments related to

- *The early ending of a pregnancy*
- *The birth of a baby born still*
- *The death of a newborn or infant*
- *The death of a child at any age*

Why do we need ritual? What is it that draws people—both known and unknown to each other—to participate in ritual when a child dies?

- *Ritual creates a community, a connection among those involved in a child's living and dying.*
- *Ritual helps create and transform meaning.*
- *Ritual may provide an understanding of seemingly unanswerable questions that flow naturally from profound grief, such as "Why my child? Why me?"*
- *Ritual provides a patterned response for adapting to change. A familiar religious ritual like baptism may be performed with simple grace in a neonatal intensive care unit. The sound of water, scooped from a bowl with a seashell, can hallow the room as it mingles with the steady beeping of another baby's monitor.*
- *Ritual has the power to transform emotions.*
- *Transformation is an outcome of ritual, yet transformation for an individual may not be visible to others.*

The power of ritual to transform the human experience at a deeply-felt spiritual level is a balm for the grieving heart.

Co-creation

This term may be new to you. *Co-creation* is a guided approach[15,16] for using ritual to transform. Because ritual grows out of relationship, we advocate for family members and caregivers to co-create (jointly create) the process and content of ritual.

Co-creation both frees the caregiver and invites the family to engage. Caregivers need not invest all **their** energy in determining what might make the best experience for the family. Through co-creation, caregivers can acknowledge family members' ability to ascertain what is most important in the moments ahead. Instead of feeling the responsibility of being in charge, the caregiver may watch to see how interactions with the family unfold or say something simple such as, "What's important to you right now?"

We define ritual as consisting of three dimensions: intention, meaning-making, and participation,[17] each of which is present in the clinical application of creating ritual. Intending to co-create ritual in response to a child's death allows each participant to feel connected to the ritual itself, to others who are present, and to the one who died. Ritual transcends, creating a bridge to a deeper, spiritual grounding. Co-creation involves actions, words, and symbols. Each serves as a springboard for meaning among the participants.

Intentions are determinations to act in a certain way. Language that implies intention has to do with what one wants to *accomplish*. In a clinical setting, one might hear a parent say, "I really want to be there when she dies" or "I intend for something positive to come out of this." When seeking opportunities for ritual, intentions of caregivers and families should be directed toward learning how to best help the family honor their relationships and shared experience. For example, the caregiver may say

- ❦ *"What would be important for you to do as a father right now?"*

- ❦ *"How would you like to honor the moments ahead of us?"*

- ❦ *"How can I help you accomplish what you want to do?"*

Ritual actions must be meaningful in a context that is acceptable and culturally respectful to participants. Caregivers should never assume what is best or right for a family but instead learn within the context of establishing relationship how to co-create ritual with the family. Rituals provide opportunity for adding new meaning or reconstructing meaning for prior life events. Objects, words, movements, and music may be used as part of a ritual. For example, a dying child's treasured bedtime story may be read one last time as parents tenderly hold their child, wrapped in a favorite blanket.

Participation is a key component of ritual. The ritual process requires doing, not just passive presence. Participation may take the form of movement, verbalization, or thoughtful reflection. The bereaved should be given the option to participate in ritual at each person's own comfort level.

Families & Ritual

The use of ritual resonates with the philosophy of family-centered care, as all members of the family benefit from participating in ritual. Children naturally go with the flow of co-creating, using their instinctive creativity to add to the richness of the experience for both children and adults.

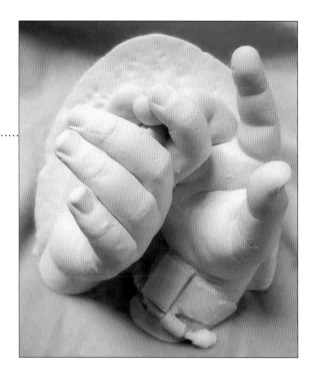

Asking a child who is old enough "How would you like to help?" or "What would you like to do?" invites a child's rich thinking to co-creation. This mold shows the hands of 4½-year-old twins, with the impression on the right made from the child who died. In this situation, the whole family made molds of their hands. The surviving twin wanted to place her hand next to her brother's, with their fingers entwined. Notice the little boy's identification bracelet and a bead bracelet on his wrist. The beads represent a related ritual. Each stands for a special connection with her brother, described in stories she shared while she strung the beads.

NOTE TO CAREGIVER:

To facilitate the use of ritual with families as a baby or child is dying, learn what is most meaningful to parents. Your recognition and support can help frame and hold the heartbreak and sadness. You might use phrases and questions such as these:

- *In your family, what usually happens when someone you love is very sick?*

- *What special moments have you and your child shared together in the past?*

- *Is there a favorite toy, song, prayer, blanket, or other comfort item we should hold in mind as we create this ritual together?*

- *How would you like to honor this time with your child?*

A 5-year-old was adamant in wanting to say good-bye to his hospitalized 2-year-old female cousin, who had died of leukemia about 2 hours before. To honor his request, his parents worked with the medical team to prepare the boy for what he would see. The little boy entered his cousin's room in his father's arms. From the high vantage point, he scanned the faces of all the adults, immediately grasping the adults' grief and somber expressions. Suddenly he looked down and saw his cousin, cradled in her mother's arms. "Put me down!" he exclaimed, running forward to touch his cousin. He whispered in her ear, "I'm going to see you again in heaven!" And then, as if he had a secret too wonderful to keep, he shouted, "We are going to see her again in heaven!" His faith-filled proclamation caused all the adults present to breathe deeply with hope. Then he did something even more amazing: He tenderly reached up, cradled his aunt's face with his small hands and said, "Auntie, are you going to be okay?" Amazingly, this little boy's actions led to the co-creation of the ritual repeated by every adult in the room. In turn, each came forward to touch the little girl, whisper words in her ear, and offer consolation to her mother.

The term "thinking outside the box" is appropriate for the way caregivers respond to families. Our openness to what parents need, want, and value—and our complete lack of judgment about what is a good idea or a bad idea—creates a sacred space for nurturing relationship. Honoring culture, personal preferences, family relationships, and parents' love for their child in this way provides the rich soil in which meaningful moments can grow.

This mother reminds us to honor the parent-child relationship. She describes how she and her family were prepared for meeting their baby, who was born with several medical conditions.

For us, she was always our child, our baby girl, our daughter. She was never "a body, a dead baby, a corpse" to prepare or dispose of. And because she was such a sick baby in utero we also knew that she would probably not appear as a normal newborn, and she didn't. This too, we prepared ourselves and our children for. But when it came down to it, none of that mattered. Amelia's appearance was of no consequence. Her disfigurement due to her condition was secondary. She was simply our daughter, our 4th child, our children's sister.

Stephanie Dyer, November, 2011

Reflection:

To help create a ritual, you could ask yourself these simple questions:

What do I (and others) want to accomplish through this?

What meaning does this have for the family? For caregivers? For me?

Who will be involved in the ritual?

What could I do to draw others in?

What materials or symbols might be used?

We hope you will fully open your heart and mind to the potential for ritual in your life and practice. Metaphors, photos, examples, and "how tos" are used to make you aware of the relationships and interactions unfolding around you. We offer this framework for ritual to launch your journey—not to prescribe it.

Ritual flows from relationship.

Relationship forms the bridge
from suffering to hope.

Hope transforms.

Metaphors

Shifting Sands

Walking along the beach or climbing across a sand dune is unpredictable. As the sand gives way to the weight of your feet, you may be moved in an unexpected direction. Areas that look easy to navigate may in reality be more difficult than you anticipated. A beautiful shell, shiny and colorful when you pick it up, may have been the source of intense pain when you stepped on it moments before. You can't go farther until you tend to the pain. Grief is like that sometimes.

Although you will eventually make your way across the sand to your planned destination, a review of your footsteps will reveal a path marked by shifts and transitions from the intended course.

Journeying with those who are dying also involves transition and change. As care shifts from curative to comfort measures, we tend to the dying with the hope of honoring patients' and families' wishes, and making life the best it can be. Throughout this journey, you will experience unexpected shifts in thinking, feeling, wishing, and hoping. Out of such shifts, ritual may arise.

"One thing is for certain," the grieving mother stated emphatically, "I cannot bear to bring any of his things home with us." She was rocking her baby son's body, looking earnestly into my eyes. "I can keep them safe for you for now," I replied. I watched as the mother gently transferred the baby into her husband's waiting arms. After some time, the mom stood over her son's hospital bed and began to straighten up his belongings. The only sound in the room was the rhythmic creaking of the rocker, and the father's gentle humming to his son. As she found an item buried under a blanket, she exclaimed, "Honey, do you remember when…" and proceeded to share a special memory of their son. I watched as this process was repeated, mom straightening up, finding an item, sharing a memory. At some point she paused, looked up and smiled, "I'm doing exactly what I thought I couldn't do! Of course I want to take his things home with us."

....

Sometimes shifts are audible, even though they may be invisible. A shift may be a big sigh or a sob breaking the silence. Letting go of pent up breath creates room for new, fresh air. Allowing ourselves to release inner pain can mark a shift or transition toward hope or healing.

Reflection:

Are you on the beach or climbing a sand dune today?

What is your grief like?

Could ritual help steady your footsteps on this journey?

 NOTE TO CAREGIVER:

Pay attention to sighs. Often after an audible exhaled breath, the one we are sitting with in silence will share significant words that may be the key to co-creating ritual.

For example: A mother who let out a tremendous sigh followed with these words: "If only she could feel sunshine on her face one last time." Out of this expression grew the opportunity for the mother and her nurse to create a ritual for her little girl to experience sunshine before she died.

Roots & Wings

The ultimate goal of parenting is to help each child find wings, providing the freedom to explore and choose how to share their gifts and talents with the world. At birth, a baby is welcomed into the immediate family, an extended family, and a larger community. Each is grounded in traditions, familiar practices, and shared beliefs. Parents strive to recognize and nurture each child's unique personality, gifts, and talents. This juxtaposition of wanting to both ground and empower forever unfolds in the parent-child relationship.

Ritual can be both grounding and empowering in the same moment. Ritual provides the opportunity to combine traditional and in-the-moment experience. Ritual requires cultural awareness. One cannot assume, but instead can engage the other by asking open-ended questions. Such assessment helps the other to identify what is already familiar and known, while also thinking mindfully, creatively, pondering "What if?"

"There are only two lasting bequests we can hope to give our children. One of these is roots, the other, wings."

Henry Ward Beecher

Naming Baby

The year 2012 is a special year for our entire family as we add two names to our family tree.

Our first child, a son, was stillborn on November 30, 1965. At that time, parents were not offered to see or hold their child because it was believed that it would be more hurtful in the long run for parents to see their baby. We were also discouraged from naming our precious baby. In 1970, that theory was still in place. Our third child, a daughter, was born still on the 17th of February. Both our babies were perfectly healthy, full-term babies, and the only explanation for their deaths was that they did not receive enough oxygen when I began to hemorrhage before they were born.

I always felt in my heart that it would have been so comforting to have met our son and our daughter in person. Both my husband and I would have so welcomed the opportunity to see and spend time with our babies. To hold and bond with each of them would have offered a great sense of comfort to us both. It would have been a way for us to show them how very much they were wanted and loved. As in all relationships we are blessed with in our lives, we needed and wanted to say "Hello" before we said "Good-bye."

While on the staff of the Resolve Through Sharing perinatal bereavement program, I learned from other parents I met that they felt naming their babies at birth gave them a sense of peace. The significance of naming the babies allowed them to be recognized as an important part of the family. Even though their parenting was limited to such a short time, it was a vital gift that only they could give their baby.

This year, my husband and I named our two babies. Our son is named Jeffrey Allen Bushek and our daughter is Malinda Ann Bushek. We, along with their brother, Brian, and their sister, Rebecca, celebrate their names being added to our family tree.

Laurie Bushek

Reflection:

How is each family member connected to the baby or child?

What grounding and empowering aspects of their relationship can be honored with ritual?

 NOTE TO CAREGIVER:

Learning what is most important to families from a cultural perspective is key to the process of co-creating ritual. Saying *Help me to know your family's traditions when someone dies* provides opportunity for reflection. It may also reveal important perspectives as the co-creation process for the ritual unfolds. If family members are separated by many miles when a child is dying, consider using technology that affords real-time communication with sound and images. For example, a laptop computer strategically placed in the room could allow a grandmother on the other side of the world to participate in Buddhist evening prayers for her dying grandchild.

Ritual provides the opportunity to combine traditional and in-the-moment experience.

Lament

Judeo-Christian tradition is rich in lament, a form of prayer that allows the release of all that feels unsettled, unfair, incomplete, and broken. Many of the Psalms in the Bible are actually laments. The psalmist trusts that God is listening to words and feelings set free by tears. Within all lament is a recognizable shift in tone from rage or anger to expression of trust in God's faithfulness and presence within the pain.

This lament was written after a series of deaths in the neonatal and pediatric intensive care units.

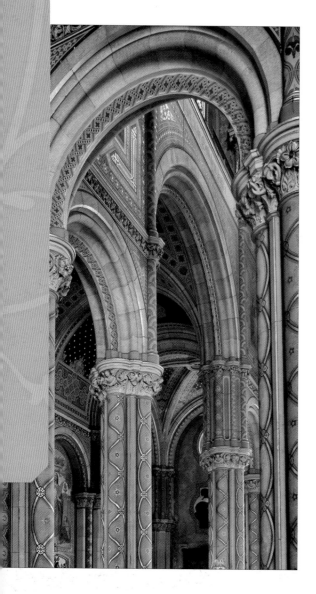

A Caregiver's Psalm of Lament

O Lord of Life, Where are You?
The silence is crushing.
In this room once filled
with the sound of pulsating heartbeats
whirring machines and
whispers of hope,
there is now only death.
The one for whom we worked so hard
lies motionless in his mother's arms.

O Lord of Healing, Where are You?
You whose mighty hand parted the sea,
gave sight to the blind,
and formed this babe in his mother's womb.
Could You not have moved
Your hand to save him?
Could You not have given us insight
to know what was wrong?
We are left to weep into our helpless hands.

O Lord of Comfort, Where are You?
Were you not beside us
as we kept our care-filled watch
over this precious one?
Did you not hear
as we whispered
words of love in his ear?
Our hearts are heavy with the weight
of our inadequacies.
All of our love and tender care
could not save him!
Why even attempt to care for another?

O Lord of Compassion, Where are You?
Move past the curtain surrounding his room.
Enter into our torrent of tears.
Break through the veil of grief
which surrounds our hurting hearts.
Have mercy, O Lord.
In this silence we will wait for you.
Let us hope in Your promise:
All who seek shall find You.

© Kathie Kobler

Keeping Silence

Sometimes intense feelings of lament cannot be expressed in words, as only silence fills the space where heartache resides. Ritual may unfold from such a silence…watching and waiting… being with unsettling feelings…finding creative ways to shift the burden of a heavy heart.

Refraining from sharing words can be powerful within ritual. Taking time for silence, asking for a time of quiet reflection, using the absence of word to honor the moment… all of these can have their soundless place in ritual, providing unique meaning known only to each participant.

In silent solitude, a grieving parent, family member, or friend might use ritual to collect and contain feelings.

Bottle of Lament Ritual

Place an empty container or bottle with a lid on a table. Quiet yourself. Take several cleansing breaths, in and out. Visualize the feelings, concerns, worries, or pains that burden your heart. Picture yourself pouring those difficult things into the empty container. Watch it fill with all of the difficulty and burden. When it is full, put on the lid and turn it until it is tight. Continue to breathe in and out. Now visualize the space in your heart once occupied by the hard things as open and ready to receive something new. In the hours to come, be conscious of what can now fill the space that has been emptied. Remember the full bottle. You know at any time you can return and reclaim the concerns and worries it contains.

Record my lament;
list my tears on your scroll —
are they not in your record?

Psalm 56:8

Reflection:

Are you waiting in silence?

Are you protesting in anguish?

Listen to words and to the silence. Could this be a meaningful moment for you?

 ## NOTE TO CAREGIVER:

Compassionate silence is a mindful approach to being with another without using words.[18] The caregiver may choose to acknowledge silence during a ritual by using words such as *"The words we hold inside speak loudly in a tone that can only be heard by the heart. We honor those unspoken words with silence."*

Circles

Circles symbolize forever. With no beginning or end, each is continuous and connected within itself. The image of a circle can be used creatively in rituals involving loss and death. Cradling, embracing, enfolding—these physical responses of parents to beloved children become circles reaching for completion. Look for ways to honor the circles that form through relationship.

Baby Billy, born still at 30 weeks.

Baby ring ritual to honor a past loss

This simple ritual can occur in private to remember a loss early in pregnancy or later… even a loss that occurred years ago but went unmarked at the time.

ITEMS NEEDED:
baby ring and neck chain
[Read these words or write words of your own.]

Baby of mine.
I remember you today as I have so often
in the years since you left me.
I place this ring on a chain that I will lovingly wear
to keep you close to my heart.
Baby of mine.

Baby ring ritual to honor relationship before or shortly after death

Baby ring blessings can also occur as the parents share tender time with their child before or after death. Like a circle, the ring has no beginning or end and can be used in ritual as a symbol of the parents' never-ending love for their baby. Parents can be presented with the baby ring using these words:

In my hand I hold a simple gold ring.
The ring is a perfect circle.
The circle is never-ending, just like your love for your child.
This love was present when you learned about your pregnancy.
This love continued as you anticipated your baby's birth.
This love has filled your baby's hospital room during each moment of hoping.
It continues, as you love your baby back to God.
Accept this ring, a symbol of your love for your baby.

The caregiver can simply extend his or her hand to present the baby ring and see what unfolds. Parents will often accept the ring, moving forward with the next step of the ritual they will co-create in the moment, placing it on their baby's finger with timing, presence, and meaning that is all their own. Parents may wish to have two rings: one buried with the baby and the other remaining with them, symbolizing the eternal relationship between parent and child.

Logan, his parents Bryanna and Paul, and Logan's caregivers

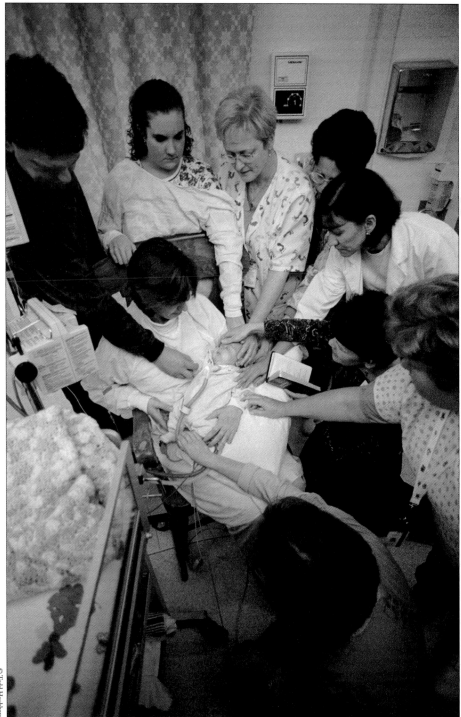

When 7-month-old Logan was dying, his caregivers spontaneously created two circles (the second is just outside the range of the camera's lens) and each took turns saying good-bye and thank-you to Logan. This image is from the conclusion of the ritual, when a chaplain read a verse of scripture, and all caregivers extended hands in a going-forth blessing.

Circles in Photographs

Bereavement photography is a ritual through which meaningful moments can be captured forever. The photographer must be both present and separate to create images in the moment. He or she silently discerns environmental elements and uses them to frame uncoached gestures and postures. Barely noticed by participants as they focus on the child, the photographer melds human subject with light, shadow, and other shapes that fill the camera lens.

Staff may gather with parents, encircling the bed or isolette of a dying premature baby, uniting the equipment and the people. Invited by their parents to draw near, brothers Kai (3) and Koa (1-1/2) created a natural circle with their newborn sister, Kanani, on their mother's bed. Captured not long before Kanani died, their mother Lisa describes this moment as "the most precious and dearest" of her life. These moments, when captured in a photograph, reflect relationship and embody emotion. Bereavement photos join living and dying in a continuous process that can be seen again and again.

Our Family
Is a circle of strength and love.
With every birth and every union the circle grows.
Every joy shared adds more love.
Every crisis faced together
makes the circle stronger.

Author Unknown

Todd Hochberg has been a documentary-style bereavement photographer since 1998. He has this to say about his approach to photography and the opportunities it affords for co-creating ritual.

For me, making meaningful photographs for families is a manifestation of presence. Through an intuitive collaboration between photographer and family, the images often make themselves. I aim to be fully present and mindful of the moment. Being present means supporting without intruding, walking with them, and following their lead as their experience unfolds.

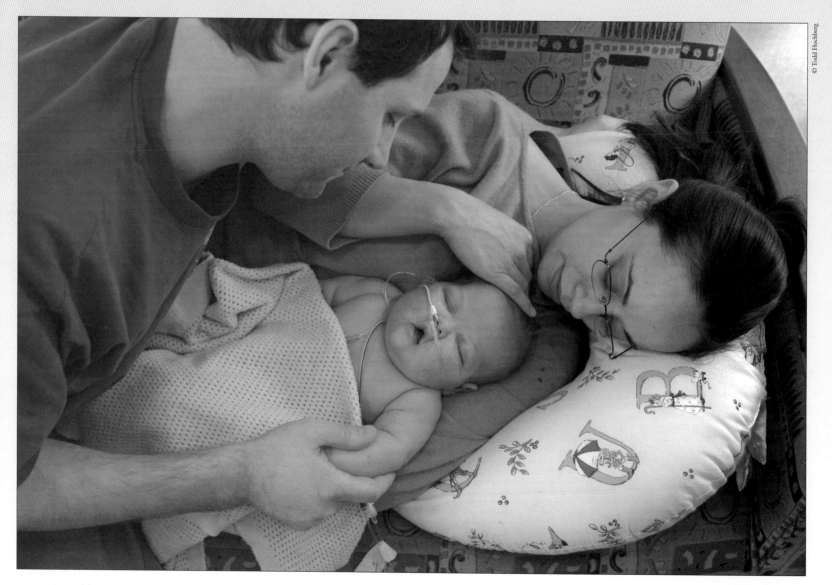

Andre and his parents

Photographers are storytellers. Documentary photography is a complementary approach to family-centered bereavement care because the photographer responds to what families are experiencing. Photographs are not staged or posed; rather photographs are tangible representations of relationship among parents, baby or child, siblings, other family members, and caregivers.

When parents view and share their pictures, they bring to mind an intimate and tender time with their child. Images showing parents creating ritual are especially powerful because they capture both relationship and emotional moments. As one mother conveyed, "We saw our time with our son laid before our eyes. It's as if the [photographs] spoke to us saying, "It was real. You did hold him. You did kiss him. You are a family.""

Among the most powerful images reflecting relationship are those showing parents creating ritual. My interest is in ritual that evolves out of experience and deep need rather than prescribed by religion, culture, or institutional protocol. These rituals are rarely discussed or planned. I am reminded of such moments: a couple enveloping their dying child on a makeshift bed in the hospital; a sibling asking to have her baby sister's handprint on her arm; a father reaching out to caress his son's head as mom offers love and assurance to her son, while lying next to him. I watch as these meaningful moments evolve and strive to capture them in photographs.

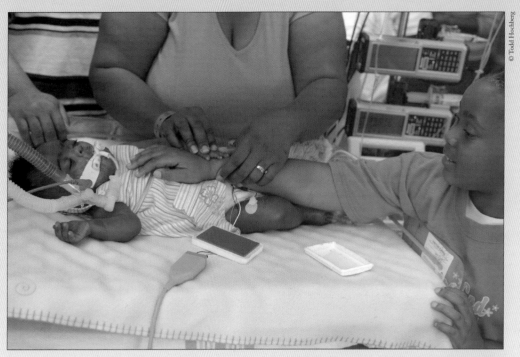

Baby Sierra with her sister Destiny

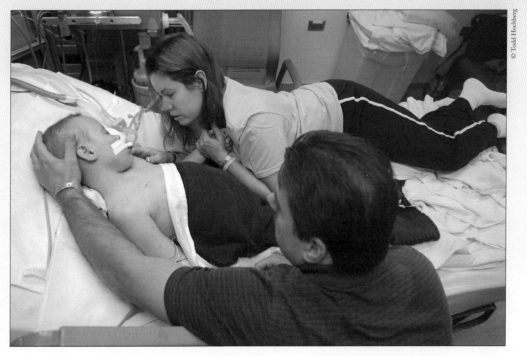

6-year-old Will with his parents

Reflection:

Have there been circles in your own experiences of grief and loss?

What did you do to draw them together?

How did you honor them?

Have you captured circles in photographs you've taken?

 NOTE TO CAREGIVER:

Circles can be the framework for meaningful moments during the days, hours, or minutes of a life drawing to its close. Watch for circles that form naturally as caregivers, family members, and friends gather to be present and meet the needs of a dying baby or child. Note the potential for physically connecting, honoring relationships, and creating community through circles. In a circle, words, prayers, songs, or silence can be shared to comfort the child and all who are joined and centered by this serene shape.

Light

Light represents the dawning of a new day: illumination, clarity, and warmth. Whether it comes from the bright sun, the gentle moon or a solitary candle's glow, each form of light may hold special meaning for a child or parent. When intentionally made part of a ritual, light creates lasting memories of a moment in time.

To Jessica

The candles are lit, but no song will be sung.
No laughter, no glee of my little one
who would have been three.

If you only knew the plans that
would be made by your dad and me.
The cake to be baked...
The presents wrapped...
and all the funny party hats.

The pictures taken by your dad of course,
as loving friends fill the house.

All of this is not meant to be,
since you were taken away from me.
No birthday cake...No presents unwrapped...
No pictures of you in your party hat.

But the candles are lit, never to go out.
For they burn forever in my heart.

Love, Mom (1982)

Circle of Light Ritual

The warm glow of flickering candles draws people in, creating a reflective ambience. When using candles for a holiday or memorial service, light a large central candle to represent love. Use this candle from one event to another or one year to the next.

Here is an example of responsorial prayer for lighting the **Candle of Love** during a memorial service:

We gather with our memories, and all our dreams and hopes. God our Parent, help us honor our children.

Let the light of love strengthen our spirits.

We gather in the light of love, but we have known great darkness. God our Parent, light our way as we grieve for our children.

The light cannot be overcome by darkness.

We gather in hope. God our Parent, heal us and care for our children.

Love never ends.

We light this candle as a symbol of our love for our children.

God our Parent, love us always as your children, give us your light and love. Amen.

Authored by Rev. Anne Edison-Albright and Rev. Carol Stephens.
Used with permission.

We come together at this moment in time
to create a community, a circle of light
to honor our children.

Create a circle of votive candles around the Candle of Love.
If you know the names of the children to be remembered in
advance, you can place the name on each votive candle. If you
don't know their names, ask each parent to name their child
after the leader says each time:

Today, and always, we remember…

Outdoor Light Ritual

Moving a dying child from the confines of a hospital room to the expansiveness of the outdoors allows natural light to bathe the child and family. For many, being outdoors symbolizes freedom and being part of a larger universe. Outdoor light is a source of beauty and strength for many who stand in its glorious rays. Others may prefer the soft, quiet light of open shade, where faces are dappled by sun sifted through leaves and branches.

This poignant story combines light and other experiences of nature. It is about one family's brief but cherished escape from the forced air of a hospital to a breezy day in the outer world.

One Small Wish

I stood in the window forcing my eyes to look as far as they could see for a sign of the vehicle that was carrying Kristin and her parents, Tom and Jean. It wasn't every day that we gave a pass to a child who was dying so that she could have a picnic at the river with her Mom and Dad. Especially this child.

We had spent endless hours isolating Kristin's fragile body from any invader. We wrapped her tiny self in kilometers of a special dressing to keep her peeling skin intact and keep the real world out. We smothered our own breath behind surgical masks and gloved our scrubbed-raw hands to dress her weeping lesions. She was her parents' dream come true; the child they longed for, planned for, and miraculously created. But the dream shattered with the diagnosis we could not change. All the love, care, and dollars in the world could not erase the truth that she would die. Was it wrong to grant even one small wish for this family? Could we not give them one day outside of her isolated space to experience the sun, the wind, the riverbank, the trees in full color; to expose her delicate eyes to what God's earth really looks like?

We decided it had to happen. Our plan included a nurse to accompany; a portable IV pump to tuck into her car seat; a day's worth of oxygen; a carefully selected sleeper, jacket, bonnet and blanket; a few hugs for each other; and the little foursome slipped out the door.

They said they'd call if they needed anything. But several hours had passed…

I caught a glimpse of the car as it neared the hospital entrance. I flew down the corridor, down the stairwell, out to the elevator and held it open as the foursome slipped back within our walls. Silently we moved as a group and quietly tucked our treasure back into her crib. Had we taken an unreasonable risk? Was I an irresponsible manager? Or had we merely created one beautiful memory for a family who deserved so much more?

The answer to my questions was evident in the eyes of her parents. I saw an early glimmer of peace, and maybe a thread of acceptance for what had to be. I went back to the window. The perfect day was turning grey, the breeze became a wind, and the leaves began to fall.

Judy Lawson, RN *(former Pediatric/Neonatal Intensive Care Unit manager)*

From *Tears Together Newsletter*, 1984

Tom and Jean Thompson, the parents in the *One Small Wish* story, provide this reflection 29 years after Kristin's death. They remind us of the meaningful moments that remain etched in memory for a lifetime.

Emotional support from family, friends, and our Gundersen Lutheran Medical Center team helped us bear the loss of Kristin and a year later, the stillbirth of her brother, Christopher. Both had the same genetic disorder. To this day, we remember those moments outside, in the light. The memories of light mingle with music to remind us of that time of trauma and pain. Lionel Richie's Stuck on You *comforted us while our daughter clung to life. Even when music evokes melancholy, mixed feelings soon give way to bittersweet but fond memories of our brief time together.*

To complete our family, we adopted 4-month-old Lynsee from Korea. Three years later, 2-month-old Chiyo arrived from Japan. The opportunity to parent them was the lasting gift we received after our loss. Lynsee and Chiyo help us remember their brother and sister through a golf tournament we sponsor each year to raise funds for Gundersen Health System, a Children's Miracle Network hospital. Our children have brought us joy and taught us a great deal about unconditional love and acceptance.

Life is so good.

Sometimes a dying child or baby cannot be taken outside. Perhaps a window or skylight can be the source of soft, natural light, even through tinted glass. Twinkle lights can be hung on the wall or on the isolette. These might have special appeal to siblings seeking a way to be involved in special preparations. Caregivers may offer real or battery-operated candles to provide light during a family ritual.

Reflection:

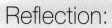

What does light mean to you?

What is your favorite kind of light?

What rituals in your own life involve light?

How does light make a difference?

Angels

For many of us, angels symbolize comfort and protection. They soar past the bounds of our everyday knowing. As messengers and signs of something beyond ourselves, they represent a surrounding force of love and care. Hospitalized children themselves have described protectors. Asking children what they see or what the protector looks like can be used to co-create a comfort ritual.

For some parents, the angel image is their child. For others, the angel was sent by God or their child as a harbinger of hope, a way of staying connected with God in the middle of a difficult time.

Some limit angels to Christian faith. In fact, these extraordinary agents are found in several faith traditions. When angels are used as part of a ritual, it is important to be sure that the parents find solace in the image of an angel. Caregivers should ask, not assume, that angels are acknowledged or meaningful to the family. For those who welcome their presence, angels and their ethereal evidence can be found in unexpected places, as this grandmother shares.

I learned right before I left for work one morning that my daughter, Ann, and her husband experienced a miscarriage the day before. I was sad to learn that I wouldn't get to meet my first grandchild. They had been trying to get pregnant for awhile and I knew that fact weighed heavily on Ann's mind when she called to tell me what happened. I left for work, aware of the bright blue summer sky with not a cloud in sight. As I was driving, I looked up and was surprised to see this single, small white cloud right above my car. For some reason, I was drawn to watch it. And there before my eyes, this small white cloud became a cross. And just as suddenly, the clear image of the cross became an angel. There it was—the sign that my first grandchild was already in heaven.

Jennifer Nordeen

The Kobler family Christmas tree

After our first baby died the evening before Thanksgiving, I returned home, exhausted with grief. My husband, wanting to comfort me, put up our Christmas tree while I slept, as he remembered how much I enjoy Christmas lights. I woke to find a lit tree, a sweet note, and one small box of ornaments. When I opened the box, there on top was a simple lace angel ornament. I couldn't bear to decorate the entire tree, but I did find the strength to choose a spot for the angel. As I stretched up my arms to hang the angel, a bit of hope met me. Since then, the angel is the first ornament I place on the tree. Many years later, one of our children asked about the ornament, so I shared how the angel helps me to remember our first baby. From then on, the story of our Christmas angel has been passed down from one child to another, which has made this such a sweet family ritual. This year, just as always, one of the kids brought me the angel ornament with a smile,

"Here you go, Mom..."

Kathie Kobler

Reflection:

Have you ever felt the presence of an angel?

Have you heard stories told by others convinced of their presence and actions?

What does the concept of guardian angel mean to you?

What is the place and purpose of angels in your faith tradition?

NOTE TO CAREGIVER:

Listen carefully when a child talks about "big shiny guys" or similar descriptors, since the child may be referring to what adults understand to be angels. Also note when parents say, "Our child will be an angel now." Honoring a family's belief in angels may provide an opportunity to co-create ritual and explore meaning.

Water

Water is essential to life. It is necessary for birth, regeneration, and renewal. Our bodies are composed primarily of water. When we are wounded physically or emotionally, water escapes from within us, flowing to the surface. It has been estimated that the body exerts a tremendous amount of energy to produce a single tear. This precious liquid can be shed during moments of extreme joy or overwhelming emotion. Whether they are evoked by sorrow or gladness, tears are a unique aspect of human expression.

Throughout history, tears of grief were often collected and saved in special containers. In Victorian times, mourners were given tiny bottles as a way to capture their tears. These ornate vessels signified the special nature of tears of grief and made it possible to set them in a place of honor. Similar designs are currently available in gift shops and could be purchased by or presented to parents as a way of honoring their tears.

Other countless tears have fallen on the ground, soaked tissues, or been brushed away by fingertips. In some cultures, though, tears are shed in private, never shown to or shared with another. Whether they are visible or hidden from view, tears should be honored.

Their presence almost always marks a significant moment.

There is sacredness in tears.
They are not the mark of weakness, but of power.
They speak more eloquently than 10,000 tongues.
They are the messengers of overwhelming grief,
Of deep contrition and of unspeakable love.

Washington Irving

Honoring tears ritual

The parents' tears may be gathered in a cotton ball, tissue, or heirloom handkerchief. A few teardrops may be carefully collected in a small shell and used to bless or baptize the child. Include a simple statement recognizing and honoring these tears of love. Verses chosen from the family's faith tradition can further enrich and deepen the experience of a ritual to honor tears. Here is one example from the Hebrew Bible:

He will swallow up death forever;
and the Lord God will wipe
away tears from all faces.

Isaiah 25:8

NOTE TO CAREGIVER:

The healthcare provider should carefully assess a family's expressions of emotions and feelings, including the presence or absence of tears. If the family is showing the depth of their experience with tears, it may be meaningful to incorporate their tears into a ritual with the baby or child.

Bathing the Body in Love

Water is also used to cleanse, renew, and refresh. Children require frequent bathing, a parental responsibility repeated countless times over the years. Yet such an ordinary task can become a transforming, meaningful moment when parents are invited to participate in the care of their child's body after death. The resources needed for this informal ritual are few and can yield priceless rewards.

It began with a simple question, "Would you like to help?" answered with a quick nod of agreement from his parents. Although we did not speak the same language, their intent was clear.

Quietly, warm water, soap, and towels were gathered. His parents slowly stood and carefully positioned his still body in the center of the bed. Together with his nurses, they paused in silence. The nurses then reached out their hands, motioning to the parents to join them in unfolding the blankets and clothing.

His parents were tentative at first, but then with a mix of reverence and eagerness, they willingly assumed their rightful roles and began to bathe his body. As his mother slipped her hands into the warm, soapy water, a faint smile touched her face. She whispered a word into his ear and began to gently wash his body. As she finished cleansing each area, his father's hands were waiting to dry the area with a soft towel. They fell into a gentle rhythm, allowing the water to wash over his wounded body while talking softly to him, followed by caressing, drying, and kissing his skin. Their faces, though streaked with tears, radiated a profound joy. They were his parents! Their willing participation in caring for their son was even more poignant, knowing just twelve months prior their newborn daughter had also died from the same devastating metabolic disorder.

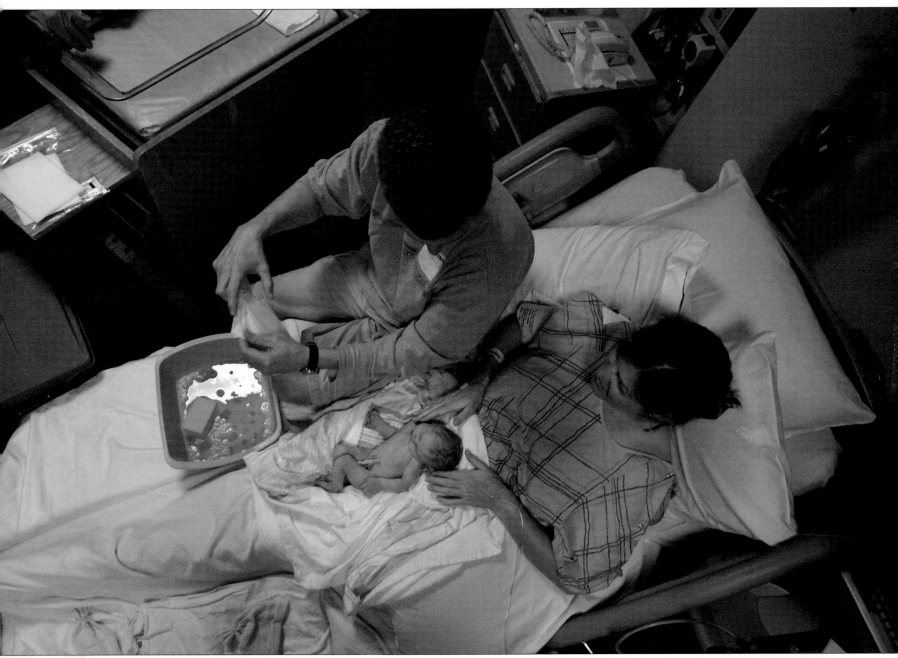

Parents prepare to bathe Luke

Reflection:

What signs and symbols do you find in water's presence or use?

How have you used water in past rituals?

How is water used in your faith tradition or spiritual life?

Word

When words are assembled in just the right way, they may capture the most profound aspects of the human experience: the joy of love, the beauty of a sunset, the depth of sorrow, the majesty of a mountaintop, the power of the sea.

Word can be an essential component of ritual. Whether spoken aloud, gently sung, repeated in unison, chanted by a cantor, or written in reflection, words shared in ritual can be powerful. Words or phrases repeated in chants or mantras can create a rhythm that helps participants focus, unite, and be wholly engaged in the moment.

Words spoken from the heart can help connect with the inexplicable, define the indefinable, feel the unimaginable, understand the incomprehensible.

Words From the Heart

Writing down feelings, stories, or reflections can be important components of a ritual to support those anticipating the death of a loved one. After putting words on paper, the writing could be read to the dying child, or—if not meant to be spoken aloud—the written words could be placed in an envelope and buried or cremated with the child.

Because of Logan

Before we met,
I was stuck in my own agenda
concerned for time
watchful of the hours

Because of You, Little One,
I was struck by the power of a moment
and humbly wondered how your soul
slipped from the constraints of our
man-made time into eternity

Before we met,
I was absorbed with my own
feelings and thoughts and concerns

Because of You, Little One,
I lost myself in your parents' pain

Before we met,
I entered your room empty-handed
equipped only with my
eyes, ears and mind

Because of You, Little One,
I left with an overflowing heart

Before we met,
I did not want to start the day
when my alarm went off

Because of You, Little One
I'm thankful for the opportunity to
have experienced this day
Thankful for the privilege of meeting
you and your family

Before we met,
I was weary

Because of You, Little One
The weariness remains
joined now by a sacred peace

Before we met,
I was taking breathing for granted

Because of You, Little One
I now quietly rest
focused on the gift of each breath

Before we met,
I was doing, moving, scattered

Because of You, Little One
I am still, present,
and overwhelmed with the power of love

August 30, 2002 2 am
© Kathie Kobler

Words from other authors or trusted sources

Parents and families may find comfort in either hearing or reading aloud from sacred texts, secular prose, and poetry. Caregivers should ask if there are any special prayers or readings that the family would wish to be shared. These can be incorporated into the child's care.

Stories & Songs

Many parents have storybooks or songs that they share with their child on a daily basis. Asking about a child's favorite bedtime story or a comforting song can lead to its use in a co-created ritual at end of life. A parent may wish to lie beside the child and read a beloved storybook. Siblings may wish to gather around the child and sing their favorite family song. Even the silliest story or song can be rich with memory or meaning when shared one last time with the dying child. Families have welcomed reading familiar books like *Goodnight Moon* or *Guess How Much I Love You* to their child and using those stories during times of transition between living and dying. One father, while reading the family's favorite story book prior to her coming off the ventilator, changed the words of *Goodnight Moon* to reflect his daughter's surroundings: "Good night NICU, good night beeps and buzzes, good night nurses whom we love."

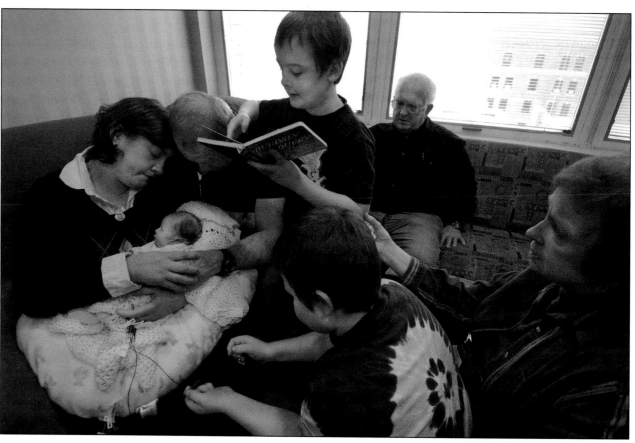

© Todd Hochberg

Big brother Liam reading to Anna

Liam, 7, came to the hospital prepared to read *The Runaway Bunny* to his sister Anna, who was dying. Once at her bedside he became apprehensive. Then spontaneously and without any coaxing, he picked up the book, stepped closer to Anna, and began reading. A sweet and poignant moment—captured in this photo—for his mother and father, who are holding Anna, brother James, and the children's grandparents.

"How much time does she have left?" her mom asked me in a weary voice.

"I'm not certain," I answered honestly, adding, "It seems as if she is soaking up all the love she can."

With a wistful smile she answered, "Yes, but there is so much more we wanted to share with her."

"Tell me more," I asked.

"I'm thinking of things we would do, places we would go, stories we would tell her," she sadly replied.

"What kind of stories?" I asked.

With that her husband, who had been silent, quickly replied, "Like how we first met. That is such a good one. She should know that…she should have a chance to know that."

Before I could speak again, this dear couple began to whisper into their daughter's ear, telling her how their lives had first been brought together. Recognizing the intimacy of this moment, I quietly exited, returning later.

By this time other family had gathered. A grandfather sat nearest the door and greeted me with a smile. "If you're coming in, you better be prepared!"

I quickly learned that the parents decided to use this time with their daughter to tell stories. Anyone wishing to enter her room could only enter after agreeing to share a story with her. Some visitors were first taken aback by such a request. But the contentedness, peace, and even joy that surrounded the little girl's bedside was palpable, radiating alike from the faces of those who shared and listened to the stories.

Word

Modeling *meaning*

Symbolizing *significance*

Encircling *emotions*

Enriching *experience*

NOTE TO CAREGIVER:

Inviting parents and others to tell stories can be a powerful way to co-create ritual. Provide time to pause, invite others to share, and allow time for those gathered to collect their thoughts. One storytelling tool can be simple heart beads. Invite all participants to choose a heart bead, while holding in mind a special story, memory, or thought about the child. Invite participants to share their reflections out loud. With each telling, place the heart bead on a string. The completed "strand of love" can be placed at the child's bedside.

Reflection:

How have words figured in your own experiences of grief and healing?

How have you invited another to share words to honor a moment?

What texts, poems, or personal writings might comfort others?

Safe Haven

Safe havens evoke the mental image of a restful presence in a location that allows one to feel secure and at home. A safe haven is a place to simply be, resting in the familiarity of memory or in comforting surroundings.

Even in the midst of an intensive care unit, one can create safe havens. Pillows and quilts draped over recliners and other comfortable chairs make it easier for tired parents to curl up and cradle an infant or older child, nestled heart to heart, head to head. Encircled in an embrace, a baby or child fills a special space in arms aching to hold onto the last hours and minutes of a sweet but all-too-short life.

> *"She fits right here," the Dad somberly shared, pointing to his chest. Yet his eyes glowed as he continued, "Every night, she fits right here and I carry her up to bed. I'm going to miss that terribly." I watched as he held his small daughter's body securely against his chest.*
>
> *Hours later, as we were discussing the direct release of her body from the hospital room to the funeral director, I remembered the Dad's words. "Would you like to carry her in your special way out to the funeral director's car?" His entire body position changed as the question hung in the air…shoulders straightened, eyes flashed with a glimmer of hope. "Would I?! Why, I'd follow you over a mile of burning coals if it meant I could do that with her one last time!" And so we did, and for one last brief moment…father & daughter were home and safe.*

For some families, the metaphor of Safe Haven means their baby or child's presence in heaven after death. Parents have taken comfort in creating ritual to prepare their little one for transition to this safe haven of heaven.

The story below illustrates one hospital's creation of a safe haven for grieving families, a room centered on reflection and comfort. This painting serves as a focal point in the room, providing a mystical centerpiece for thoughts and emotions.

The pastoral painting, "Heaven's Garden," is laden with spiritual symbolism. In this unique work commissioned by St. Vincent's Perinatal Bereavement program, "Journey," the imagery of artist Laurie Snow Hein expresses thoughts and feelings shared by bereaved families. The original design concept was developed by Lynette Spruiell, Journey and Resolve Through Sharing coordinator.

Each person who enters the Eric Blake Faulkner Quiet Room is drawn to Hein's color-drenched tableau. A softly burbling slate and copper water feature seems to animate a waterfall in the scene. Through a large stained glass window, muted light bathes the room's comfortable furnishings in hues that echo the painting's natural tones. Woodsy-scented potpourri and a carpet patterned in soft, moss green vines invite every visitor to step out of the "real world." This is a soundproofed sanctuary from the joyful noise of families celebrating in the labor and delivery area. Although used primarily for grieving families, the room is also appropriate for baptism or blessing rituals as well as physician consults when unexpected outcomes occur.

The painting was designed to minister to persons of many faiths. The children represent various ages and cultures. No full faces are shown so family members can gaze at the painting and imagine their loved ones being nurtured in the peaceful afterlife portrayed by Hein's eloquent brushstrokes. Symbols such as water, rock, light, lamb, rose, and sparrow are grounded in many spiritual traditions. Each image has poetic or scriptural meaning.

Time after time, the quiet room and painting fulfill their shared purpose. Family members overcome with grief are taken to the room to recover. Once they are seated, their breathing slows and they begin to relax. If staff remain quiet and let the room speak, the bereaved often find their own words to begin their healing process. As one grandmother stated, "This room seems to lay a gentle hand on the stark reality of our loss."

Lynette Spruiell, LPN

Despite terminal illness, an outgoing 10-year-old boy continually charmed family and caregivers. In anticipation of his dying, his parents shared their faith in God and heaven. In his last days, the typically talkative youngster withdrew in deep sadness and silence. Then one day, he confided his fear: "How will I recognize all my relatives in heaven?" His family quickly gathered photos of relatives, many of whom had died long before the boy's birth. At first, he intently studied the photos and learned their names. A few days later he tearfully confided to his nurse he was worried that heaven would be boring because everyone there was old. With his parents' consent, the nurse told him she knew children his age who were already in heaven. With the consent of those children's parents, snapshots of prospective playmates were shared. Each night the boy looked through his stack of prints, thinking of new friends he would soon meet. All of the photos brought him comfort. They were eventually displayed together in a place of honor at his wake.

Reflection:

If you were creating a safe haven, what would it look and feel like?

What is your own vision of heaven and other safe havens?

Transitions

Transitions are like knitting, weaving together relationships and creating connections. A transition encompasses change, good-byes, and welcomes. Sometimes families learn during pregnancy that the expected baby has a condition that will cause death before birth or shortly after. Ritual can help a family get ready for both. Here is a way of welcoming a new baby who may not live long.

Ritual of welcome

Gather together all family members and friends who would like to welcome the expected baby. Ask each to bring an item or words written on a piece of paper that represents something significant in the family's life or the person's relationship to the baby or other family members. Pass a travel bag or small suitcase from one person to the next. Let each participant talk about what they place in the bag and why it is precious. When everyone is finished, all will say together:

*We welcome you into our family,
no matter how short your time
with us will be (has been).
We want you to be loved,
to be comforted,
to be pain free.*

Blessing Way

Knowing that a baby will die usually allows time for creating special rituals. The Blessing Way ritual, designed to honor a mother's upcoming birth, can be adapted for a mother who is pregnant with a baby known to have a life-threatening condition. The purpose of the Blessing Way is to nourish the mother, which can be done in a variety of ways: foot washing, hand massage, gifts, written messages, and food.

 NOTE TO CAREGIVER:

Caregivers do the best they can in preparing families for how their baby may look or what the baby's living and dying may be like. In doing so, we may make assumptions about parents' experiences that are different from their reality. We know parents who wished they would have been better prepared.

Stephanie's story *(next page)* reminds us that the best approach is probably one that engages the parent in how much—or how little—information they need or want. When you ask "Would you like me to tell you more about what your baby will look like?" or "Would you like more information on what your baby's actual dying may be like?" you put the decision about information in the parent's hands. When you let them lead the way, you build trust. Trust is the cornerstone of any relationship.

Stephanie's family chose a unique setting for a transition ritual—their home. Amelia Rose spent four days at home after she died, lovingly cared for by her family.

Our Final Goodbye

By Stephanie, mother of Amelia Rose, posted on her blog:

In the quiet of this sleepy morning, I sit next to my Amelia Rose. This morning will be our goodbye. Today will be the final one for me in this journey of letting go. Today, my baby girl will be forever changed and gone ~ physically ~ from my life. No longer will I be able to hold her, caress her, bathe her in my tears. Never again will I know what the softness of her skin feels like or be able to breathe in her sweet baby smell. My lips will not brush against her forehead anymore. My eyes will never see her again. My arms will never cradle her, rock her, or be able to reach for her again. My neck will never feel her weight snuggled against it. My heart will never be the same again. It is fractured and broken. I am so very grateful for the blessing of our choice to keep her home with us. We have had four days with Amelia. Four days as a family. Four days with all four of our children together. The unpleasant things that those uncomfortable with our choice warned us about…NEVER HAPPENED! She is perfect, with rosy cheeks, soft skin, and a peaceful expression. She looks as if she is asleep. We were prepared for less time. We kept thinking that we only would have one day with her, that the change of death would happen too fast in her small and fragile little body. And it hasn't! She looks the same as the day I issued her forth into this world.

It has not been scary for our children. The opposite, in fact. Aiden, Oliver, and Marin have been able to experience death in a way that most adults never do. We have been able to share Amelia with them, answer all their questions, and give them time to be with their sister.

They have only ever loved her, want to kiss her, hold her, and tell her their stories. Saying goodbye today will be hard for them as well, but the time we have had, has given us memories more precious than I could have imagined! We have given our children the most precious of gifts. TIME to say goodbye, on their terms. Still, the goodbye is breaking my heart! Holding her in the last minutes until she has to go is all I can do. Crying will have to suffice. I just wanted to write this down so that I can remember this in the blur of days to come. The months and years ahead without her…are unimaginable right now.

Now, in the last precious minutes, I want to soak up the moment into my skin and make it a part of me forever. The blanket she is wrapped in, the hat that has graced her head, the jewelry she wears…will be what we have left. They could not possibly be enough, but it is all we will have. So, for now, I will hold onto her body. I will cradle her in my arms one last time. I will kiss her endlessly before she leaves. I will inhale deeply and try and remember her smell. I will desperately pray that I can let her out of my arms and share her with the rest of my family. They will need to say goodbye too. But I am feeling very selfish right now and cannot bear to let her go.

This is the end. Our final moments together. As the minutes pass, they are perfect and sweet and precious. They are exquisitely painful and heavy at the same time. I can feel the time slipping away ~ it is alive (almost electric) in these last moments.

http://beyondwordsdesigns.com/?p=1484   (Reprinted with permission.)

NOTE TO CAREGIVER:

Touching Hands Ritual of Transition:

After the death of their baby or child, family members often express concern as they contemplate leaving the hospital. Consider offering to place an ink print of the child's hand on the palm of the grieving parent's or sibling's hand in preparation for this transition. This is a way for family members to "hold" the child's hand as they walk into the outside world. One mother took a picture of the ink print in her palm and had it recreated as a tattoo. This lasting image of a parting ritual comforts her to this day.

Reflection:

In what ways have you welcomed a special child into your life?

Think about final moments you have experienced. What was the time like for you? What memories do you carry in your heart?

Bridges

The photo illustrates a foundational understanding of bridges: What one sees while crossing is only a portion of the entire bridge. The part beneath, often forgotten, holds the bridge in place, allowing it to function as a connector. Bridges link one place with another. Metaphorically, bridges can be used to link the present and future, the present and past, and life and death. Ritual is also a bridge. The transforming power of ritual does not end after the death has occurred. Ritual can become a trusted pathway, a tangible connection to the one who has died. Evidence of ongoing ritual can be found if one looks or listens carefully. Examples include

- *A roadside memorial to a teen who died in an accident*

- *A special nook or area where mementos of a child are displayed in a home*

- *Serving a special cake each year on the birthday of a child who died*

- *A visit to the gravesite*

- *Tending a memorial garden.*

Sometimes the very act of honoring memories of someone who died involves ritual. Jessica was 18 when she died in a car accident, killed by a driver who fell asleep. Jessica's mother, Jean, chose to honor her through a photo quilt, which served as a bridge to the family's memories of Jessica.

[Jessica Lynn Dowdell-Miller]
June 10, 1987 to January 28, 2006

A Keepsake Quilt for Jessica

Jessica was just a very special young lady with a zest for life you couldn't put into words. I had to do something, and the idea of making keepsake quilts in Jessica's memory felt right, a gift from me to her to show her how much I love her and miss her.

It was heartbreaking at times to work on them, but it was also a healing process I needed to go through. When I gave my daughter, Maggie, who is two years older than Jessica, her quilt, I have never seen a more wonderful expression on my daughter's face. For one short moment, the love that I felt from Maggie when she received this quilt took away all the pain of losing Jessica.

Photo Quilt Instructions:

Here are the directions, with a few tips that helped me create three beautiful quilts, one for each of her siblings: Maggie, Ted, and Jeremy.

Purchase inkjet printable fabric in white from a craft store. Determine the size of the finished quilt. I used 35 photos, 7 portrait and 28 landscape. Follow instructions for printing photos onto the fabric. I used "best" quality printing, which meant four ink cartridges per quilt.

Choose material for the background that has a comparable weight to what you use for the photos. Take the landscape photos and sew one strip of material across the top and one across the bottom to make them the same height as the portrait-oriented photos. Press in the same direction on each block and always on the back side of the picture.

Next, lay them out and sew into rows. Sew a row of sashing onto the bottom of each row and onto the top of the first row (I used 2.5"-wide strips). Add the border, cutting it to the size wanted for the overall quilt. Sew width ends first and then lengths. Press after each end is sewn on and do a final pressing of the whole quilt from the back side.

Use a flat bed sheet (180-200 thread count) for the backing, several inches larger than the top. Assemble it back to front, pinning it to a quilt rack or taping it

Guests at the parents' memorial service for their twins Ian and Shane were invited to bring perennials to create this memory garden. As the parents continue to tend the garden, they remember and honor their sons.

tightly to a carpeted floor. Next add a layer of batting, followed by the quilt top. Pin through the batting and the back. Use yarn in coordinating colors to tie sashing strips in each corner and one in the center above and under each photo. Remove the quilt from the rack or floor, stitch in the ditch around the last seam of the border, and sew binding onto the quilt. Fold at seams as the photos wrinkle easily. Hang it overnight to remove the wrinkles.

Symbols as Bridges to Memory

Some families may hold dear a special toy or other symbol that represents their child. They may include this item in future family photos. Families may also incorporate these symbols into tangible acts or remembrances that bring comfort, serving as connections to beloved children over time.

Bereavement Services chose a leaf, floating on water, as a symbol of grief and grieving. The upturned leaf contains a small droplet, perhaps dew or a tear, depending on one's interpretation. For Jamon, the leaf became a bridge to remembering her daughter.

My daughter Zoe was born at 10:05 p.m. on Saturday, May 22, 2004. She died at 10:08 p.m. the same night. I got to hold her while she took one of her first breaths and I was holding her when she took her last. Her time was short but her memory will remain with me forever. Since Zoe was born I have been blessed with two more children. Every day I can look at them, laugh with them, and share with them my life and they do the same with me.

While I was grieving for Zoe I knew I needed something that her and I could share and would be special to the two of us. I was given sympathy cards, molds of her hands and of her feet. My aunt made her a blanket and a dress to be buried in. While these things are very special to me they are not something I can take with me wherever I go. This beautiful tattoo on the back of my neck is something I will always have and be able to share. When people comment on my tattoo I get the opportunity to talk about her and how she blessed my life.

Hospital staff placed a card on the door to my hospital room. It featured a fallen leaf, a very beautiful and thoughtful way of letting people know that those on the other side of the door are quite possibly having the worst day of their life (and we were). And I picture that leaf when I think of her and I think that having that symbol on my body will always remind me of this beautiful little girl who was with us for such a short time and yet remains in our hearts forever.

*A symbol may
connect parents to children:
those who live with them and
those who live only in their hearts.*

Brian & Jen Linse

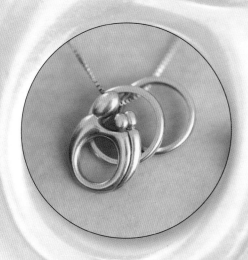

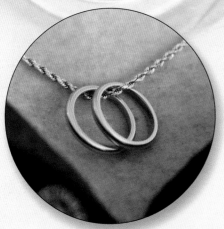

Jen writes: *Brian and I have two boys, born 3 years apart. Between the boys, we had two miscarriages. I wear a necklace that symbolizes our 4 children. The "mother with two children charm" was given to me following the birth of our second son. It represents the unconditional love of a parent and child. I received a gold band from my nurse after each miscarriage. I wear the two gold bands with the charm to acknowledge the same absolute love I felt during my two pregnancies that resulted in early pregnancy losses and the love I feel for our sons.*

Brian writes: *There are many feelings experienced with a miscarriage: grief, loss, sadness, pain, frustration, and self-doubt. After each of our miscarriages, a nurse presented rings to both my wife and me as a means of recognizing the loss we felt—the "what-could-have-been." The rings, for me, were the lost story; however, they evolved to also become symbols of the two children we do have as well as our marriage, our relationship, and our journey. It was comforting to leave the hospital with something—not close to what we hoped for, but something that helped us get through that initial pain and the self-reflection that followed.*

Signs as Bridges to Memory

Signs offer hope and portray ongoing relationship. Signs are reported by caregivers as well as parents, often bringing great comfort to those receiving their awaited confirmation or acknowledgement. Some parents believe their child communicates with them through signs such as a dragonfly, feather, or coin. Happening upon the object unexpectedly may be used by the bereaved as recognition their child is okay.

In 1999, I lost my first son to SIDS. One night, several weeks after Justin died, my husband and I were driving in the car. It was a clear, crisp night and it seemed as if all of the stars were visible in the sky. I asked God for a sign that Justin was all right. That he had made it to Heaven…and was all right. I waited and waited all that drive home…but nothing.

Every time a new baby is born into our family, my mom makes Christmas stockings for that baby's first Christmas. After Justin died my mom didn't know what to do…she asked if we still wanted a stocking made for Justin and we said, "Yes."

Justin's siblings with his stocking: Jack, Isabella, and Elliot

The next time my husband and I went to visit my parents, my mom told me she had completed Justin's stocking. She told me how it had been so hard for her to try and decide what to put on his stocking. She said one day she was sitting thinking about him and how she could make his stocking just right. Then she felt a hand on her shoulder and just knew what it had to be. She brought out the stocking…dark blue with a light blue angel in the middle and surrounding it, several sets of silver stars. I immediately thought of that night with the star-filled sky when I asked for a sign that Justin was all right. Here was my answer, on a Christmas stocking, which my mother somehow magically created to coincide with my desperate search to learn of my son's well-being.

Needless to say, I had gotten my sign.

Heidi Giese

The pink ribbon in the center was tied on the wreath by Madelin Grace's mother, Patricia Wiley.

During a 2012 Resolve Through Sharing bereavement training in perinatal death, a tearful woman suddenly left the room. Jill Wilke, Bereavement Services lead educator, followed her to provide comfort and learn why a slide showing a ribbon wreath provoked such a strong response. Patricia Wiley explained the wreath had a pink ribbon bearing the name of her baby, Madelin Grace—a ribbon tied with her own hands about a year before during the RTS 30th anniversary celebration in La Crosse. At the time of Madelin's death, circumstances had kept Patricia from having a service with immediate family. She considered the 30th anniversary's ribbon-tying ritual and butterfly release a personal service for her baby. Patricia was amazed and honored to see her daughter's name as part of the RTS training she now shares with others.

NOTE TO CAREGIVER:

Many hospitals provide memorial services, remembrance walks, and hospital burials. Each of these has important symbolism and meaning for a community of the bereaved and their caregivers, serving as a bridge of support and hope that honors relationship over time. Caregivers who provide follow-up bereavement support may ask parents "What has become meaningful to you? What brings you comfort?" Listen for ritual and symbolism (e.g., sleeping with a child's favorite toy, blanket, or outfit; noting that seeing a butterfly is a "sign" from their baby that she is okay).

Reflection:

Caregivers and parents grieving their child's death can ask these kinds of important questions:

What are you doing to remember your baby?

How do you stay connected to your child?

In what ways do you find comfort each day?

Ritual for Caregivers

Those who care for families when a child dies witness the sorrow and suffering of others. Just as with families, ritual for caregivers can be co-created, arise in the moments surrounding significant experiences, or be planned in advance.

Moments that may give rise to ritual:

  🌿 *Multiple deaths on the unit in a short time*

  🌿 *Traumatic patient encounter*

  🌿 *Loss of a long-term, beloved patient*

  🌿 *Disconnection among team members due to a heavy workload*

Planned responses that may give rise to ritual:

  🌿 *Recognition of staff commitment to their daily care of patients*

  🌿 *Blessing of caregivers' hands*

  🌿 *Rededication of a unit space*

  🌿 *Staff memorial service*

> *Do not close your eyes before suffering. Find ways to be with those who are suffering by all means… awaken yourself and others to the reality of suffering in the world.*
>
> Gautama Buddha

The Caregiver's Final Good-bye

Suffering is a state of intense distress, generally involving physical, emotional, or spiritual pain. Pediatric and perinatal healthcare professionals witness the suffering of others and experience personal suffering.[1] According to Ferrell and Coyle, "nurses have described their role as helping those who are suffering become whole."[1(p.74)]

Suffering affects the whole person, influences or is influenced by relationships, and has the power to transform.[1,19]

Ritual can play an important role in allowing healthcare professionals to process their own suffering and to grieve. Papadatou[19] asserts that caregivers grieve and that grief is transformative. She also makes the key point that grief varies between experiencing and avoiding the sense of loss. Caregivers who are not able to let go of the intensity of grief, at least for brief periods, are more likely to experience complications of grief. Ritual that binds caregivers together and creates community in the midst of loss is a balm for the hurting heart and contributes to the transformation from pain to hope. When the timing is right, ritual can also help to release their feelings so they can move on to care for other patients. Papadatou notes:

> *Formal or informal ritual activities help them affirm their bonds with each other and enhance connectedness and a sense of belonging to a team that is able to contain suffering and provide opportunities for change and growth.*[19(pp.264-265)]

As a nurse, one of the saddest times after a death is when the family has left the hospital, and I'm carefully preparing their child's body for eventual transfer to the funeral director. This time is a final act of care and usually unfolds in a timely fashion.

I still cannot fully capture with words what tugged at my heart one particular evening when I could not finish this task of preparing a small body. An unsettling urge overtook me as I could not bear to move forward with my work...

On Rocking Arthur

The room seems so empty now,
I am left holding you.
Your family has gone,
But traces of their tears are evident
in the dampness of your clothes.
Their whispers of love
still hang in the air.

I sink into the rocking chair,
cradling your motionless body
in my arms.
Together we rock.

You are so beautiful,
your face and body perfectly formed.
It is hard to believe that inside
you were too broken and sick
to remain long on this earth.
Tears fall as I think of all
your poor body has suffered & endured
in the fight to live.

Minutes pass, and then an hour.
For some unknown reason,
I am unable to stop rocking you.

I have sung to you,
prayed for you,
thanked you for allowing me
to have a small part in
your short life.

But still, I am unable to put you down.

Friends peek around the curtain,
their worried looks convey
the unspoken words of concern…

The rhythm of our rocking is broken
by the familiar ring of the telephone.
It is your Mother.
Crying,
wishing she could tell you
of her love just one more time.

She thinks you are already far away…

Smiling through tears, I gently reply,
"We've been waiting, shall I put the receiver close to him?"

Faint strains of a lullaby drifted upwards…
We had arrived.

© Kathie Kobler

Caregivers experience many significant moments and emotions when a baby or child dies. Out of such experiences, ritual may arise, offering staff the opportunity to honor relationship and their grief. For example, caregivers may choose to do one of the following:

🌿 *Nurses often join together to prepare a child's body for the funeral director. Such tender, caring moments may offer opportunity to pause and reflect aloud on the special ways the nurses connected with the child.*

🌿 *A prayer, blessing, or simple words may be spoken as a child's body leaves the unit.*

🌿 *A single rose can be laid at the bed space where a death occurred for a period of time.*

🌿 *Hanging a picture of an angel or star in a special spot on the unit can alert incoming staff that a death has occurred.*

🌿 *An organized prayer, blessing, or simple words of renewal may be used over a room or area of the unit where multiple deaths have occurred. One hospital chose to completely redecorate the room on their labor and delivery unit after the devastating, unexpected death of a mother and her baby.*

🌿 *A memorial service for staff-only can be planned to honor children who have died during the past year. Staff may choose to light candles or release balloons or butterflies as they honor the precious lives they are remembering.*

Marcia Jenkins, RN, monarch butterfly release ritual at Resolve Through Sharing's 30th anniversary.

Unit Blessings

Sometimes hospital units experience patient deaths in rapid succession. Heartache may be pervasive and palpable, as teams are present to successive grieving families. Staff may ask to have the unit blessed after such periods of unrelenting sadness. The next ritual, written and led by chaplain resident Tracy Nolan, M. Div., offered NICU nurses and residents the opportunity to acknowledge three deaths in less than 24 hours.

In a beautiful example of co-creation, team members responded in an unexpected way when Tracy invited them to touch something in the unit: They reached out and held onto each other as the ritual unfolded.

I know that the last few weeks, and even just the last few days, have been incredibly difficult here in NICU. We've lost too many little ones. Angie asked me to lead us in a blessing of this space, particularly Pod C, as we enter into this new day and remember God's presence—the presence of something or someone bigger than us all—in this place.

So, to start, would you join me in **prayer**?
Loving God, we come to you with sadness and we are striving for trust.
Be present here in this place, this Pod where, you know, pain has come so deeply.
Grant your presence that this would be a place free of pain and instead filled with peace.
Grant your presence that this whole NICU would be a place free of fear and instead filled with trust.
Grant your presence that we would be filled with your spirit.
Be here with us now, and always. Amen.

As I was thinking about what it means to bless this space, I recalled the ways I have seen you all bless this space every day – with the care and love that you give to all of these little ones, every hour. So – it would only be appropriate that your hands are the hands of blessing in this space today. As you're able, I **invite you to place a hand** on a wall, a condo, a crib, a desk, a chair, and join me as we bless the space, together. I'll speak a word of blessing, and each time I say *"We say…"* I'd ask you to repeat: *"Peace and healing be present here."*

These walls of Pod C have seen too many tears, God. Families, friends, and we ourselves have felt pain and desperation. Make the tears, pain, and desperation of this space be no more. No more. We say… **Peace and healing be present here.**

We know that you are a God of love, whose intention is always love, whose presence is always love. Fill this space with that steadfast love and overcome anything that is NOT love. We say… **Peace and healing be present here.**

Our hands and hearts are tired from weeks of losses. We ask for energy, wisdom, and guidance as we daily enter into this work, our work of blessing. Through our hands, we say… **Peace and healing be present here.**

Above all, we know that you lead us – through valleys of death, and, into green pastures. Make this place a green pasture, restore our souls, and be with each person – youngest and oldest – in this unit. Make your blessing be known. And so we say… **Peace and healing be present here.**

Amen.
Go in peace today, embraced by God's peace. Go in peace today, surrounded by friends.
Amen.

Touchstones for Ritual

A hospital team may choose to keep specific supplies on hand that can be used as end-of-life situations unfold on the unit. The final section of this book will describe items that may serve as touchstones, along with corresponding ideas so caregivers can co-create their own rituals. Many of these items can be found online and/or purchased at a local craft supply store. Caregivers are encouraged to consider their favorite verses or lines of poetry that could be incorporated into the ritual. A few rituals are offered in their entirety as examples of how ritual can be customized to meet the individual needs of caregivers following shared experiences of loss and grief.

Candle

Battery operated flicker candles are safe to use in the hospital setting and come in a variety of sizes. They can be used to honor significant events or the deaths of patients.

For example, a candle can be used at the start of a unit meeting to honor those patients who have died or who have touched the team's heart since the last unit meeting. Staff can be invited at the start of the meeting to call to mind the baby or child they would like to remember. After a few moments of silent reflection, the leader can say, "We light this candle to remember and honor those who have brought light and love into our lives."

Hope Chest/Treasure Chest Ritual

A small wooden/wicker chest or box can serve as a meaningful container to hold words written by ritual participants.

For example, the treasure chest could be placed in a significant place on the unit after a child's death. Small pieces of colored paper can be placed next to the chest. Written instructions placed nearby can invite staff to write a few words or draw a picture that represents a special memory of the patient. The completed papers may be folded and placed in the chest as reminders of ways staff will continue to treasure their memories of the child.

Sand

Sand can provide an especially effective touchstone after difficult situations leave staff feeling drained, uncertain, or overwhelmed about next steps. Sand can be placed in a shallow glass dish or pan. The words below refer to the shifting sands metaphor on p. 15 and can be read aloud:

Walking along the beach or climbing across a sand dune is unpredictable. As the sand gives way to the weight of your feet, you may be moved in an unexpected direction. Areas that looked easy to navigate may in reality be more difficult than you anticipated. A beautiful shell, shiny and colorful when you pick it up, may have been the source of intense pain when you stepped on it moments before. You can't go on until you tend to the pain.

Although in the end we will make our way through the sand to arrive at our planned destination, a review of our footsteps will reveal a path marked by shifts and transitions from our intended course. Journeying with sick children and their families involves enduring transition and change.

Over the past [two weeks], we have experienced difficulty and uncertainty. [You may choose to add a description here of the shared situations that have prompted the ritual.] There may have been times

when you have felt weary, especially when no end to the hurt and pain seemed in sight. You may have experienced unexpected shifts in your thinking, feeling, wishing, and hoping. [Pause for a few moments for private reflection.]

Before us is a circle of sand. You are invited to come forward, as you are ready, to place your hand in the sand. As you set your hand in the sand, press down. Notice how the sand shifts underneath your weight. Notice too, how eventually your hand settles into the sand, finding a safe resting spot. Before you step away, notice how your hand print overlaps with the other imprints. [Invite staff to come forward one by one to press their hands in the sand.]

[Call everyone's collective attention to the sand.] See how our individual prints have responded to the presence of others. Amidst shifting sands, we are all intertwined, present to help each other through the difficult situations we are facing. In our collective presence, as shown in the sand, we see unified, solid, centered spaces. May this image be called to mind as we continue to move through this difficult experience. Remember we are present for each other. May this centering ritual offer hope, meaning, and healing. May the work of your hands and hearts continue to be blessed.

River Stones

River stones of varying shapes, color, and sizes can be offered as a touchstone in ritual. The stones could represent whatever you wish. Here is an example of using the stones as "courage stones."

Stones have been in existence for countless years, enduring harsh conditions and severe transitions as the seasons unfold. Yet they have kept their consistency and beauty through hard times. [Invite all participants to choose a stone. Ask them to look closely at the stone they have chosen.] Note the unique size, color, texture of your stone. Feel its heaviness or lightness in your hand.

Now cup the stone in your hand. Notice how the stone changes in temperature because of your presence.

Reflect on a situation in which you provided strength or comfort for another in need of care.

Just as this stone absorbs your warmth and changes because of your presence, so does each hurting individual benefit from your presence and care. Even when you cannot stop pain or suffering, your willingness is a priceless gift.

Accept this stone as a gift. It is a courage stone, a symbol of strength and resilience. When you hold this stone…

- *May you believe in your resilience during difficult situations*

- *May you find the strength you need to be present to those who hurt*

Poetry

Reflective writings such as poetry can be used as a touchstone in ritual. For example, when staff is hurting, these words written by Emily Dickinson could be offered as a reflective reading during ritual:

Hope

Hope is the thing with feathers
That perches in the soul,
And sings the tune—without the words,
And never stops at all

~Emily Dickinson

White Feathers

It is often helpful to provide a symbol participants can receive during the ritual and use at a later time as a touchstone to reflective memories. Simple white feathers can be laid out on a table and offered during ritual. This may be done in combination with Emily Dickinson's "Hope" poem.

Feathers can be a helpful touchstone after staff members on the unit have experienced much turmoil or distress.

Before you today is a white feather. You are invited to pick up your feather. Hold it in your hand as you listen to this reflection:

Feathers are delicate, light in weight and fragile in appearance. Feathers shift with the slightest movement, accommodating their position as a result of even the slightest breeze. Yet despite their appearance, feathers are incredibly strong. Together feathers accomplish an amazing feat: They can lift a bird in flight to incredible heights.

Just like each of you….you tirelessly shift to meet the needs of your patients. Your presence provides an incredible gift to those who hurt. May the work of your hands and hearts continue to be blessed.

Scratch Art Hearts or Stars

At times during ritual, it may be important for caregivers to reflect on special qualities of a child who has died or to recall specific memories shared. For moments such as these, paper scratch art may be used to encourage creative expression. These scratch art products come in a variety of shapes with bright colored paper hidden under a black coating. Participants can use the scratch tool while writing or drawing, resulting in beautifully colored words or designs. The completed art can be strung together and hung in a special place on the unit.

Multi-colored Glass Beads

Staff members can be invited to string beads of different colors and shapes to create "strength bracelets." The information below describes the meaning of each color of bead. Staff members should be instructed to choose beads that represent their work with patients and families. After the beads are strung, invite participants to share how they chose their beads as each connects to their work. The ritual of beading and telling stories provides a touchstone for staff members in the moment and after as they wear the bracelets.

Making Bead Bracelets to Inspire & Build Strength

This bead activity is intended to allow you to reflect on the important work that you do. Ask yourself these questions:

What inspires you? What gives you strength or courage in your work? As you think about these questions, choose beads that carry meaning to you to construct a symbolic piece of jewelry. This bracelet can be taken with you when you leave today as a daily reminder of the strength you possess. Identifying what gives you courage is one way to honor your work.

The guide at right describes color symbolism. It is not meant to limit you in your bead selection process. Colors can have different meanings to everyone, so be creative!

COLOR GUIDE

Yellow: Intellectual energy, optimism, sunshine, relaxation, stress relief

Blue: Spiritual awareness, tranquility, peace, inspiration, comfort, peaceful dreams

Red: Physical energy, good fortune, adventure, love, ambition, courage

Green: Powerful energy of nature, growth, healing, hope, rejuvenation, balance

Gold: Good health, happiness, success, true friends, wisdom, wealth, God

Turquoise: Creative expression, imagination, relaxed, self-awareness, initiative

Black: Dramatic presence, confidence, strength, protection, power

Silver: Female power, draws out negative energy, telepathy, distinguished

Orange: Friendliness, intuition, creativity, celebration, courage

Purple: Enchantment, respect, transformation, charisma

Brown: Nurturing, home, dependable, healing, simplicity

White: Purity, serenity, silence, new beginnings, balance, harmony

Pink: Admiration, grace, thanks, inner peace, emotional healing

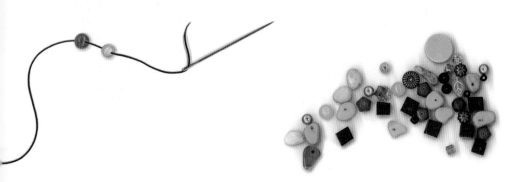

Dissolving Paper & Water: Release Ritual

There is a unique paper product that dissolves instantly when coming in contact with water. It looks like regular paper, can be written upon in a regular fashion, and only transforms when it is placed in water. Dissolving paper can be a very useful tool for rituals of transformation. Here are two examples of how the dissolving paper can be used:

[Set the table with a large pitcher of water and an empty glass bowl.]

Provide each participant with a 1-inch x 2-inch strip of dissolvable paper. Do not let participants know anything about the paper other than it will be used to write on. Make sure each participant has a pen.

Share the following words:

We continually engage in the ongoing journey of taking in and letting go. Our bodies resonate with its rhythm. Our hearts beat and relax, our lungs expand and release.

We invite you to settle into your chair and take a few cleansing, deep breaths...in...out...

We gather to honor relationship, between each other, between the children and families in our care. As we enter into another's suffering we are present, taking in their pain, doing our best to give back... pouring out our care with compassion, understanding, and support.

VERSION ONE – Water added at beginning.

(can be used after staff has experienced difficult situations)

[As the words about pouring out are read, empty the water from the pitcher into the bowl.]

We invite you now to take up the piece of paper before you. Think about your experiences with families. Think about something that has been difficult for you, something that you wish to lay down, something you wish you could change. Write down a few words, or draw an image that represents what you are holding in mind.

When you are ready, we invite you to come forward and place the paper in the water. Use your finger to touch and submerge the paper. Swirl the water. Watch what happens…

[Participants come one by one to the water, experience their paper and written words dissolving into the bowl. You may wish to play instrumental music during this portion of the ritual.]

[After everyone has finished dissolving their paper, say the following words…]

In this act of release and transformation, we open new spaces within ourselves. This now empty pitcher represents those new spaces. We are emptied, to be filled again.

[End of version one]

VERSION TWO – Water added at end.

(can be used as a community honoring ritual)

We invite you now to take up the piece of paper before you. Think about your experiences with families. Think about what you hope for…consider what ways you appreciate collaborating with colleagues and your wishes for your team in the future. Think about what brings you meaning. Write down a few words, or draw an image that represents what you are holding in mind.

When you are ready, fold your slip of paper, and come forward to place it in this empty bowl. Then take a place around the table.

[When everyone is in place around the table, share these words.]

This bowl represents the coming together of our hopes, dreams, and wishes. We are a community, united together in the common bond of wanting to provide the best possible care for our patients.

[Pick up the pitcher, and share these words.]

This water represents our combined compassion, energy, and heart for this work…

[Empty the contents of the pitcher into the bowl, swirl as needed, or invite participants to join in swirling the water. Let all observe in silence, then invite reflection.]

How was this for you? What did you experience? What is on your mind?

[Allow participants time for processing this powerful ritual…enjoy hearing the meaning they have found through the joining of the water and paper. Provide closing words that acknowledge their work, the gift of combined strength and compassion that are theirs as they continue to support one another in this work.]

A Bridge For Caregivers

Caregivers willingly enter into a vulnerable place with patients and families. As they provide care, their own feelings and experiences are called forth. As caregivers pause, reflect, acknowledge, and are mindful, they honor their own grief. In doing so, they release past experiences and create a bridge to a relationship with their next family.

Reflection:

In what ways can team members support

each other when a patient dies?

What are we currently doing?

What could be added?

NOTE TO CAREGIVER:

We invite you to come back to these two pages after being with a family and child at the end of life. Consider using the PRAM framework as you allow the photo to draw you in.

Pause. Imagine yourself on the bridge in the photo.

Reflect on what you have experienced with this patient's death.

Acknowledge what you will carry with you and the gifts left behind by this child and family.

Be **Mindful** of the steps you will take on the bridge as you anticipate entering into relationship with the next family.

Final Invitation

Like the impact of ritual described in its pages, this book has no real conclusion. Instead, we leave you with the thoughts, images, and reflections we hope you carry with you as you find, co-create, and participate in meaningful moments. When you co-create, you may never fully understand the meaning that ritual can have for another. The power to transform and be transformed exists in all of us.

Ritual flows from relationship.

Relationship forms the bridge
from suffering to hope.

Hope transforms.

References

1. Ferrell BR, Coyle N. *The Nature of Suffering and the Goals of Nursing*. New York: Oxford University Press; 2008.

2. Anderson M. *Sacred Dying: Creating Rituals for Embracing the End of Life*. New York: Marlowe; 2003.

3. Romanoff BD, Terenzio M. Rituals and the grieving process. *Death Stud*. 1998;22(8):697-711.

4. Romanoff BD, Thompson BE. Meaning construction in palliative care: the use of narrative, ritual, and the expressive arts. *Am J Hosp Palliat Care*. 2006;23(4):309-316.

5. van Gennep A. *The Rites of Passage*. Chicago: The University of Chicago Press; 1960.

6. Rando TA. *Parental Loss of a Child*. Champaign, IL: Research Press Co; 1986.

7. Driver TF. *The Magic of Ritual: Our Need for Liberating Rites that Transform Our Lives and Our Communities*. San Francisco: HarperSanFrancisco; 1991.

8. Brin D. The use of rituals in grieving for a miscarriage or stillbirth. *Women & Therapy*. 2004;27(3/4):123-132.

9. Côté-Arsenault D. Weaving babies lost in pregnancy into the fabric of the family. *Journal of Family Nursing*. 2003;9(1):23-37.

10. Grout LA, Romanoff BD. The myth of the replacement child: parents' stories and practices after perinatal death. *Death Stud*. 2000;24(2):93-113.

11. Meert KL, Briller SH, Schim SM, Thurston C, Kabel A. Examining the needs of bereaved parents in the pediatric intensive care unit: a qualitative study. *Death Stud*. 2009;33(8):712-740.

12. Milstein JM. Introducing spirituality in medical care: Transition from hopelessness to wholeness. *JAMA*. 2008;299(29):2440-2441.

13. Doka KJ. The role of ritual in the treatment of disenfranchised grief. In: Doka KJ, ed. *Disenfranchised Grief: New Directions, Challenges, and Strategies for Practice*. Champaign, IL: Research Press; 2002:135-147.

14. Perry B. Why exemplary oncology nurses seem to avoid compassion fatigue. *Can Oncol Nurs J*. 2008;18(2):87-99.

15. Limbo R, Kobler K. The tie that binds: Relationships in perinatal bereavement. *MCN Am J Matern Child Nurs*. 2010;35(6):316-321; quiz 321-323.

16. Pridham KF, Limbo R, Schroeder M, Thoyre S, Van Riper M. Guided participation and development of care-giving competencies for families of low birth-weight infants. *J Adv Nurs*. 1998;28:948-958.

17. Kobler K, Limbo R, Kavanaugh K. Meaningful moments: The use of ritual in perinatal and pediatric death. *MCN Am J Matern Child Nurs*. 2007;32(5):288-295; quiz 296-297.

18. Back AL, Bauer-Wu SM, Rushton CH, Halifax J. Compassionate silence in the patient-clinician encounter: a contemplative approach. *J Palliat Med*. 2009;12(12):1113-1117.

19. Papadatou D. *In the Face of Death: Professionals Who Care for the Dying and the Bereaved*. New York: Springer; 2009.

We invite you to share stories of
ritual and reflection you experience
as a result of reading our book.

Please send them to:

ritualandreflection@gmail.com

(Photographs are welcome, too.)

About the Authors

Rana Limbo, PhD, RN, PMHCNS-BC, FAAN, is associate director, Resolve Through Sharing, Bereavement and Advance Care Planning Services, Gundersen Health System, La Crosse, Wisconsin. She has been involved in perinatal bereavement work as a nurse since 1981. She was the first coordinator of Resolve Through Sharing®, the premier international hospital-based perinatal bereavement program. She is the author of numerous articles and book chapters. Her first book, co-authored with Sara Wheeler, When a Baby Dies: A Handbook for Healing and Helping, published in 1986, is considered a classic and is widely used by parents and professionals. She is a Fellow of the American Academy of Nursing and an elected member of the International Work Group on Death, Dying, and Bereavement.

Kathie Kobler, MS, APN, PCNS-BC, CHPPN, serves as the advance practice nurse leader of the perinatal and pediatric palliative care programs at Advocate Children's Hospital Park Ridge, IL campus. She has been caring for medically fragile and dying infants and children since 1985. She speaks and writes professionally on perinatal and pediatric palliative care and bereavement issues. She works on a national level to promote the growth of perinatal and pediatric palliative care, currently serving in leadership roles on the National Board for Certification of Hospice and Palliative Nurses and the National Pediatric Hospice and Palliative Care Collaboration.